Glencoe McGraw-Hill

Math Connects

Course 2

Chapter 1
Resource Masters

Consumable Workbooks Many of the worksheets contained in the Chapter Resource Masters booklets are available as consumable workbooks in both English and Spanish.

	MHID	ISBN
Study Guide and Intervention Workbook	0-07-881054-X	978-0-07-881054-1
Skills Practice Workbook	0-07-881053-1	978-0-07-881053-4
Practice Workbook	0-07-881056-6	978-0-07-881056-5
Word Problem Practice Workbook	0-07-881055-8	978-0-07-881055-8

Spanish Versions

	MHID	ISBN
Study Guide and Intervention Workbook	0-07-881058-2	978-0-07-881058-9
Skills Practice Workbook	0-07-881057-4	978-0-07-881057-2
Practice Workbook	0-07-881060-4	978-0-07-881060-2
Word Problem Practice Workbook	0-07-881059-0	978-0-07-881059-6

Answers for Workbooks The answers for Chapter 1 of these workbooks can be found in the back of this Chapter Resource Masters booklet.

StudentWorks Plus™ This CD-ROM includes the entire Student Edition test along with the English workbooks listed above.

TeacherWorks Plus™ All of the materials found in this booklet are included for viewing, printing, and editing in this CD-ROM.

Spanish Assessment Masters MHID: 0-07-881061-2 ISBN: 978-0-07-881061-9
These masters contain a Spanish version of Chapter 1 Test Form 2A and Form 2C.

Send all inquiries to:
Glencoe/McGraw-Hill
8787 Orion Place
Columbus, OH 43240

ISBN: 978-0-07-881041-1
MHID: 0-07-881041-8

Math Connects, Course 2

Printed in the United States of America.

2 3 4 5 6 7 8 9 10   009   16 15 14 13 12 11 10 09

Contents

Teacher's Guide to Using the Chapter 1 Resource Masters

The *Chapter 1 Resource Masters* includes the core materials needed for Chapter 1. These materials include worksheets, extensions, and assessment options. The answers for these pages appear at the back of this booklet.

All of the materials found in this booklet are included for viewing and printing on the *TeacherWorks Plus*™ CD-ROM.

Chapter Resources

Student-Built Glossary (pages 1–2) These masters are a student study tool that presents up to twenty of the key vocabulary terms from the chapter. Students are to record definitions and/or examples for each term. You may suggest that students highlight or star the terms with which they are not familiar. Give this to students before beginning Lesson 1-1. Encourage them to add these pages to their mathematics study notebooks. Remind them to complete the appropriate words as they study each lesson.

Family Letter and Family Activity (pages 3–6) The letter informs your students' families of the mathematics they will be learning in this chapter. The family activity helps them to practice problems that are similar to those on the state test. A full solution for each problem is included. Spanish versions of these pages are also included. Give these to students to take home before beginning the chapter.

Anticipation Guide (pages 7–8) This master, presented in both English and Spanish, is a survey used before beginning the chapter to pinpoint what students may or may not know about the concepts in the chapter. Students will revisit this survey after they complete the chapter to see if their perceptions have changed.

Lesson Resources

Lesson Reading Guide Get Ready for the Lesson reiterates the questions from the beginning of the Student Edition lesson. Read the Lesson asks students to interpret the context of and relationships among terms in the lesson. Finally, Remember What You Learned asks students to summarize what they have learned using various representation techniques. Use as a study tool for note taking or as an informal reading assignment. It is also a helpful tool for ELL (English Language Learners).

Study Guide and Intervention This master provides vocabulary, key concepts, additional worked-out examples and Check Your Progress exercises to use as a reteaching activity. It can also be used in conjunction with the Student Edition as an instructional tool for students who have been absent.

Skills Practice This master focuses more on the computational nature of the lesson. Use as an additional practice option or as homework for second-day teaching of the lesson.

Practice This master closely follows the types of problems found in the Exercises section of the Student Edition and includes word problems. Use as an additional practice option or as homework for second-day teaching of the lesson.

Word Problem Practice This master includes additional practice in solving word problems that apply the concepts of the lesson. Use as an additional practice or as homework for second-day teaching of the lesson.

Enrichment These activities may extend the concepts of the lesson, offer an historical or multicultural look at the concepts, or widen students' perspectives on the mathematics they are learning. They are written for use with all levels of students.

Graphing Calculator, Scientific Calculator, or Spreadsheet Activities These activities present ways in which technology can be used with the concepts in some lessons of this chapter. Use as an alternative approach to some concepts or as an integral part of your lesson presentation.

Assessment Options

The assessment masters in the *Chapter 1 Resource Masters* offer a wide range of assessment tools for formative (monitoring) assessment and summative (final) assessment.

Student Recording Sheet This master corresponds with the Test Practice at the end of the chapter.

Extended-Response Rubric This master provides information for teachers and students on how to assess performance on open-ended questions.

Quizzes Four free-response quizzes offer assessment at appropriate intervals in the chapter.

Mid-Chapter Test This 1-page test provides an option to assess the first half of the chapter. It parallels the timing of the Mid-Chapter Quiz in the Student Edition and includes both multiple-choice and free-response questions.

Vocabulary Test This test is suitable for all students. It includes a list of vocabulary words and 10 questions to assess students' knowledge of those words. This can also be used in conjunction with one of the leveled chapter tests.

Leveled Chapter Tests
- *Form 1* contains multiple-choice questions and is intended for use with below grade level students.
- *Forms 2A and 2B* contain multiple-choice questions aimed at on grade level students. These tests are similar in format to offer comparable testing situations.
- *Forms 2C and 2D* contain free-response questions aimed at on grade level students. These tests are similar in format to offer comparable testing situations.
- *Form 3* is a free-response test for use with above grade level students.

All of the above mentioned tests include a free-response Bonus question.

Extended-Response Test Performance assessment tasks are suitable for all students. Sample answers and a scoring rubric are included for evaluation.

Standardized Test Practice These three pages are cumulative in nature. It includes two parts: multiple-choice questions with bubble-in answer format and short-answer free-response questions.

Answers

- The answers for the Anticipation Guide and Lesson Resources are provided as reduced pages with answers appearing in red.
- Full-size answer keys are provided for the assessment masters.

1 Student-Built Glossary

This is an alphabetical list of new vocabulary terms you will learn in Chapter 1. As you study the chapter, complete each term's definition or description. Remember to add the page number where you found the term. Add this page to your math study notebook to review vocabulary at the end of the chapter.

Vocabulary Term	Found on Page	Definition/Description/Example
algebra		
algebraic [al-juh-BRAY-ihk] expression		
arithmetic [air-ith-MEH-tik] sequence		
base		
coefficient		
defining the variable		
domain		
equation [ih-KWAY-zhuhn]		
equivalent expressions		
evaluate		
exponent		
factors		

1 Student-Built Glossary (continued)

Vocabulary Term	Found on Page	Definition/Description/Example
function [FUNK-shuhn]		
function rule		
numerical expression		
order of operations		
perfect squares		
powers		
radical sign		
range		
sequence		
solution		
square		
square root		
term		
variable		

1 Family Letter

Dear Parent or Guardian:

One of the most frustrating things for young mathematics students is that they often do not see how what they learn in class will be useful to them in the real world. This math class will make every effort to relate topics we learn in the classroom to the world outside the classroom.

In **Chapter 1, Introduction to Algebra and Functions**, your child will learn about powers and exponents, squares and square roots, operations, variables and expressions, equations, properties, sequences, and functions. In the study of this chapter, your child will complete a variety of daily classroom assignments and activities and possibly produce a chapter project.

By signing this letter and returning it with your child, you agree to encourage your child by getting involved. Enclosed is an activity you can do with your child that practices how the math we will be learning in Chapter 1 might be tested. You may also wish to log on to **glencoe.com** for self-check quizzes and other study help. If you have any questions or comments, feel free to contact me at school.

Sincerely,

Signature of Parent or Guardian _____ Date _____

1 Family Activity

State Test Practice

Fold the page along the dashed line. Work each problem on another piece of paper. Then unfold the page to check your work.

1. Simplify the expression shown below:

$$7 + 4(12 \cdot 3) - 4^2$$

What is the value of the above expression?

A 380
B 135
C 143
D 7

2. Find the value of position n for the table below.

Position of Term	Value of Term y
1	1.75
2	3.5
3	5.25
4	7
n	?

Which equation will give the value of term n?

A $y = 1.75n$
B $y = 1.75 + n$
C $y = n + 1.75n$
D $y = 2.75 - n$

Fold here.

- -

Solution

1. *Hint: Use order of operations when simplifying a problem that has multiple operations in it. 1. Perform all operations in parentheses and operations that involve exponents. 2. Complete multiplication and division operations. 3. Complete addition and subtraction operations from left to right.*

1. Do $12 \cdot 3$ and 4^2 first. You should now have $7 + 4(36) - 16$.
2. Do $4(36)$ next. You should now have $7 + 144 - 16$. Therefore, this is the correct answer.
3. Go from left to right for the addition and subtraction remaining. $7 + 144 = 151; 151 - 16 = 135$.

The answer is **B**.

Solution

2. *Hint: Find the relationship between the position and value of the terms on a table. Always look beyond the first pairing. You should always check your idea with at least three pairings to be sure it is correct. Substitute the values in the table into each equation to find the best fit.*

A $y = 1.75n$

$1.75 = 1.75(1)$ ✓

$3.5 = 1.75(2)$ ✓

$5.25 = 1.75(3)$ ✓

The answer is **A**.

1 Carta a la familia

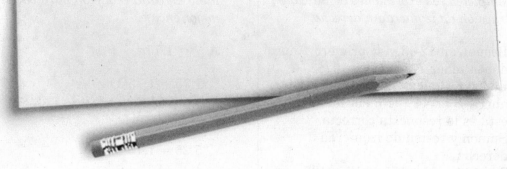

Estimado padre o apoderado:

Una de las cosas que más decepcionan a los alumnos de matemáticas jóvenes es no ver a menudo cómo lo aprendido en clase puede serles útil en la vida real. Esta clase de matemáticas pondrá todo el esfuerzo necesario en relacionar los temas que se aprendan dentro del aula con el mundo que la rodea.

En el **Capítulo 1, Introducción al álgebra y funciones**, su hijo(a) aprenderá sobre potencias y exponentes, cuadrados y raíces cuadradas, operaciones, variables y expresiones, ecuaciones, propiedades, sucesiones y funciones. En el estudio de este capítulo, su hijo(a) completará una variedad de tareas y actividades diarias y es posible que trabaje en un proyecto del capítulo.

Al firmar esta carta y devolverla con su hijo(a), usted se compromete a ayudarlo(a) a participar en su aprendizaje. Junto con esta carta, va incluida una actividad que puede realizar con él(ella) y la cual practica lo que podrían encontrar en las pruebas de los conceptos matemáticos que aprenderán en el Capítulo 1. Además, visiten **glencoe.com** para ver autocontroles y otras ayudas para el estudio. Si tiene cualquier pregunta o comentario, por favor contácteme en la escuela.

Cordialmente,

Firma del padre o apoderado _____ Fecha _____

1 Actividad en familia

Práctica para la prueba estatal

Doblen la página a lo largo de las líneas punteadas. Resuelvan cada problema en otra hoja de papel. Luego, desdoblen la página y revisen las respuestas.

1. Reduzcan la siguiente expresión:

$$7 + 4(12 \cdot 3) - 4^2$$

¿Cuál es el valor de la expresión anterior?

A 380
B 135
C 143
D 7

2. Hallen el valor de posición de n en la tabla siguiente.

Posición del término	Valor del término y
1	1.75
2	3.5
3	5.25
4	7
n	?

¿Qué ecuación dará el valor del término n?

A $y = 1.75n$
B $y = 1.75 + n$
C $y = n + 1.75n$
D $y = 2.75 - n$

Doblen aquí.

- -

Solución

1. *Ayuda: Usen el orden de las operaciones para simplificar un problema con múltiples operaciones. 1. Realicen todas las operaciones en paréntesis y las que tengan exponentes. 2. Completen las expresiones de multiplicación y división. 3. Completen las expresiones de adición y sustracción de izquierda a derecha.*

1. Resuelvan $12 \cdot 3$ y 4^2 primero. Ahora deben tener $7 + 4(36) - 16$.
2. Luego resuelvan $4(36)$. Deben tener ahora $7 + 144 - 16$. Por lo tanto, esta es la respuesta correcta.
3. Sumen y resten de izquierda a derecha.
   $7 + 144 = 151; 151 - 16 = 135$.

La respuesta es **B.**

Solución

2. *Ayuda: Hallen la relación entre la posición y el valor de los términos en una tabla. Siempre miren más allá del primer par. Para asegurarse de que la idea sea correcta, deben probarla por lo menos con tres pares. Reemplacen los valores de la tabla en cada ecuación para encontrar el mejor encaje.*

A $y = 1.75n$

$1.75 = 1.75(1)$ ✓

$3.5 = 1.75(2)$ ✓

$5.25 = 1.75(3)$ ✓

La respuesta es **A.**

1 Anticipation Guide

Introduction to Algebra and Functions

Step 1 *Before you begin Chapter 1*

- Read each statement.
- Decide whether you Agree (A) or Disagree (D) with the statement.
- Write A or D in the first column OR if you are not sure whether you agree or disagree, write NS (Not Sure).

STEP 1 A, D, or NS	Statement	STEP 2 A or D
	1. When solving math problems, all the information given in the problem should be used.	
	2. The exponent of 4 is 1.	
	3. Numbers written with exponents are in exponential form.	
	4. The square of a number is found by finding a factor that multiplied by itself will equal the number.	
	5. The number 24 is a perfect square.	
	6. All operations within grouping symbols should be evaluated first in an expression.	
	7. The expression $(3 + 1)^2$ is equal to $3^2 + 1^2$.	
	8. The expression $8n + 4n - 6$ contains two terms.	
	9. The solution to an equation is any number that makes the equation true.	
	10. An example of the Identity Property of Multiplication is $6 \times 9 = 9 \times 6$.	
	11. In an arithmetic sequence, each term is found by adding the same number to the previous term.	
	12. A function table is a way to organize the input and output numbers of a function.	

Step 2 *After you complete Chapter 1*

- Reread each statement and complete the last column by entering an A (Agree) or a D (Disagree).
- Did any of your opinions about the statements change from the first column?
- For those statements that you mark with a D, use a separate sheet of paper to explain why you disagree. Use examples, if possible.

1 Ejercicios preparatorios

Introducciónal álgebra y a las funciones

PASO 1 *Antes de comenzar el Capítulo 1*

- Lee cada enunciado.

- Decide si estás de acuerdo (A) o en desacuerdo (D) con el enunciado.

- Escribe A o D en la primera columna O si no estás seguro(a) de la respuesta, escribe NS (No estoy seguro(a)).

PASO 1 A, D o NS	Enunciado	PASO 2 A o D
	1. Al resolver problemas matemáticos, se debe usar toda la información dada en el problema.	
	2. El exponente de 4 es 1.	
	3. Los números escritos con exponentes están en forma exponencial.	
	4. El cuadrado de un número se halla al encontrar un factor que multiplicado por sí mismo sea igual al número.	
	5. El número 24 es un cuadrado perfecto.	
	6. En una expresión, se deben evaluar primero todas las operaciones dentro de símbolos de agrupamiento.	
	7. La expresión $(3 + 1)^2$ es igual a $3^2 + 1^2$.	
	8. La expresión $8n + 4n - 6$ contiene dos términos.	
	9. La solución a una ecuación es cualquier número que haga verdadera la ecuación.	
	10. Un ejemplo de la propiedad de identidad de la multiplicación es $6 \times 9 = 9 \times 6$.	
	11. En una sucesión aritmética, cada término se encuentra sumando el mismo número al término anterior.	
	12. Una tabla de funciones es una manera de organizar los números de entrada y de salida de una función.	

PASO 2 *Después de completar el Capítulo 1*

- Vuelve a leer cada enunciado y completa la última columna con una A o una D.

- ¿Cambió cualquiera de tus opiniones sobre los enunciados de la primera columna?

- En una hoja de papel aparte, escribe un ejemplo de por qué estás en desacuerdo con los enunciados que marcaste con una D.

1-1 Lesson Reading Guide

A Plan for Problem Solving

Get Ready for the Lesson

Read the introduction at the top of page 25 in your textbook. Write your answers below.

1. Do you have all of the information necessary to solve this problem?

2. Explain how you would solve this problem. Then solve it.

3. Does your answer make sense? Explain.

4. What can you do if your first attempt at solving the problem does not work?

Read the Lesson

5. In which step of the four-step plan do you decide which strategy you will use to solve the problem?

6. What does the four-step plan suggest you do if your answer is not correct?

7. Complete the sentence: Once you solve a problem, make sure your solution contains any appropriate _____.

Remember What You Learned

8. Think of a way to help you remember the names of each of the steps of the four-step plan in the correct order. For example, try writing a sentence using all of the words.

1-1   Study Guide and Intervention

A Plan for Problem Solving

Four-Step Problem-Solving Plan

When solving problems, it is helpful to have an organized plan to solve the problem. The following four steps can be used to solve any math problem.

1. **Understand** – Get a general understanding of the problem. What information is given?

2. **Plan** – Select a strategy to solve the problem and estimate the answer.

3. **Solve** – Carry out your plan to solve the problem.

4. **Check** – Determine the reasonableness of your answer compared to your estimate.

Example 1   Use the four-step plan to solve the problem.

RECREATION A canoe rental store along the Illinois River in Oklahoma has 30 canoes that it rents on a daily basis during the summer season. If canoes rent for $15 per day, how much money can the store collect for canoe rentals during the month of July?

Understand   You know that they rent 30 canoes per day for $15 each. You need to determine the total amount of money that can be collected during the month of July.

Plan   First, find the total amount of money that can be collected each day by finding the product of 30 and 15. Next, multiply the previous result by 31, the number of days in July. You can estimate this result by 30. $30 \times 15 \times 30 = 13,500$

Solve   Since $30 \times \$15 = \$450$, the canoe rental store can collect $450 in rental fees each day. This means the total amount of money that could be collected during the month of July is 450×31 or $13,950.

Check   Is your answer reasonable? The answer is close to the estimate of $13,500.

Exercises

Use the four-step plan to solve each problem.

1. **MONEY** Colin works for his dad during summer vacation. His dad pays him $5.20 per hour and he works 20 hours per week. How much will Colin earn during his 8-week summer vacation?

2. **BOOKS** A student assistant in the school library is asked to shelve 33 books. If he puts away 9 books the first hour and then 6 books each hour after that, how long will it take him to shelve all 33 books?

3. **SHOPPING** Alicia bought a $48 sweater on sale for $25 and a $36 purse on sale for $22. How much did Alicia save?

4. **MAIL** It cost Ramon $3.73 to mail a package to his grandmother. The post office charged $2.38 for the first pound and 45 cents for each additional pound. How much did the package weigh?

1-1 Skills Practice

A Plan for Problem Solving

Answer these questions about the four-step problem-solving plan.

1. During which step do you ask if your answer makes sense?

2. During which step do you revise or make a new plan if your first plan doesn't work?

3. During which step do you select a strategy for solving the problem?

4. During which step do you ask yourself, "What do I need to find out?"

Choose one of the following to describe how you would plan to solve each problem. Do not solve the problems.

A. Use only one operation, such as addition or multiplication.

B. Use a combination of operations, such as division and addition.

C. Use a different strategy.

5. **MONEY** Julia opened a savings account with a deposit of $36. She then deposited $5 per week for one month. If she then withdrew $9.50, how much is left in her savings account?

6. In how many different patterns can 3 rose bushes, 2 sunflowers, and 5 tulip plants be planted in a garden?

7. Use the four-step plan to solve Exercise 5.
   A. Understand

   B. Plan

   C. Solve

   D. Check

1-1 Practice

A Plan for Problem Solving

Use the four-step plan to solve each problem.

1. **ENGINES** A car engine turns 900 revolutions per minute while idling. How many revolutions does a car engine turn in one second while idling?

2. **DISTANCE** While traveling in Montana from Butte to Sidney, Mr. Kowalski, recorded that the distance from Butte to Sidney was about 6 times the distance from Butte to Bozeman. Bozeman lies between Butte and Sidney. If the distance from Butte to Bozeman is 82 miles, what is the approximate distance from Bozeman to Sidney?

3. **NUMBERS** What are the next two numbers in the pattern?
   3.1, 3.11, 33.11, 33.111, _____ , _____

4. **TIDES** The Bay of Fundy in Nova Scotia, Canada is known for large tides. On a particular day low tide was at 2.3 feet. The tide then rose 6.6 feet every hour for the next six hours. What was the height of high tide on that particular day?

5. **BASKETBALL** If team A won by 2 points what was the number of points scored by team A in the 3rd quarter?

Team	Quarter Scores 1st 2nd 3rd 4th				Final Score
A	21	18	?	17	?
B	15	19	20	25	79

6. **COOKING** A cake recipe requires a total 16 tablespoons of butter for one cake, some for the batter and some for the frosting. If 4 tablespoons of butter are needed for the batter for one cake, how many tablespoons of butter are needed for the frosting if Samantha wants to bake three cakes?

1-1 Word Problem Practice

A Plan for Problem Solving

Lesson 1-1

MAGAZINES For Exercises 1 and 2, use the table that shows the costs of several popular magazines.

Costs of Popular Magazines		
Magazine	**Cost of Yearly Subscription**	**Cost of a Single Copy**
Teen World	$9.98 (12 issues)	$3.25
Soccer World	$19.97 (6 issues)	$4.99
Book Nation	$19.98 (12 issues)	$2.99
TV Weekly	$46.28 (52 issues)	$1.95

1. How much could you save by buying *Teen World* with a yearly subscription rather than 12 single copies?

2. Which of the magazines saves you the most money by purchasing a yearly subscription instead of an equivalent number of single copies? How much will you save?

3. **BICYCLING** Adriana can ride her bicycle 6 miles in one hour. How long will it take her to ride 15 miles?

4. **BASKETBALL** At Johnson Middle School an average of 500 people attended each of the 15 home basketball games. If admission was $3 per person, about how much money was collected in all?

5. **THEATER** A local theater has floor seating, balcony seating, and box seating. If the theater contains 2,500 seats with 425 seats in the balcony and 215 box seats, how many seats are on the floor?

6. **POPCORN** Janelle plans to buy three boxes of popcorn at the movies for herself and two friends. If each box costs $1.95, how much change will she receive when she pays with a ten-dollar bill?

1-1 Enrichment

The Great State Mystery

The United States of America has not always had 50 states. The states gradually joined the Union, starting with the first state in 1787 to the most recent state in 1959. The tables lists 15 states and their populations based on the 2000 Census. Use the 6 clues given and a problem solving process to complete the table below.

Delaware	783,600	Iowa	2,926,324	New York	18,976,457
Georgia	8,186,453	Louisiana	4,468,976	Ohio	11,353,140
Hawaii	1,211,537	Mississippi	2,844,658	Texas	20,851,820
Illinois	12,419,293	New Jersey	8,414,350	Wisconsin	5,363,675
Indiana	6,080,485	New Mexico	1,819,046	Virginia	7,078,515

1. The first state to enter the Union has the least population of the states listed.

2. The states beginning with the letter 'I' were the 19th, 21st, and 29th states admitted to the Union. Iowa entered the Union 30 years after Indiana.

3. New Jersey and Georgia were among the original thirteen colonies. Their entry number is the same as the digit in the hundreds place of their population.

4. Hawaii, Texas, and Wisconsin were the 28th, 30th, and 50th states admitted to the Union, but not in that order. To find their order, put them in order from greatest to least population.

5. The state with the second largest population entered the Union 15 years before Ohio and 24 years before the state with a population in the 4 millions.

6. The day of the month that Mississippi was admitted into the Union can be found by dividing its order of entry by 2.

Order of Entry	State Name	Date of Entry
1		December 7, 1787
3		December 18, 1787
4		January 2, 1788
10		June 25, 1788
11		June 26, 1788
17	Ohio	March 1,
18		April 30, 1812
	Indiana	December 11, 1816
20	Mississippi	December , 1817
21		December 3, 1818
		December 29, 1845
29		December 28, 1846
		May 29, 1848
47	New Mexico	January 6, 1912
		August 21, 1959

14

1-2 Lesson Reading Guide

Powers and Exponents

Get Ready for the Lesson

Read the introduction at the top of page 30 in your textbook. Write your answers below.

1. How is doubling shown in the table?

2. How many text messages will be sent after 4 minutes?

3. What is the relationship between the number of 2s and the number of minutes?

Read the Lesson

4. What is the difference between a power and an exponent?

5. Identify the exponent in each expression.

   a. 5^8

   b. 8^5

   c. 8^3

   d. 8

6. Complete the sentence:
   Numbers written with exponents are in _____ form, whereas numbers written without exponents are in _____ form.

Remember What You Learned

7. In the expression 6^7, circle the exponent in red. Then circle the power in another color.

Lesson 1–2

1-2 Study Guide and Intervention

Powers and Exponents

$$\underset{\text{Base}}{\uparrow}3^{\overset{\text{Exponent}}{\nearrow}4} = \underbrace{3 \cdot 3 \cdot 3 \cdot 3}_{\text{common factors}} = 81$$

The **exponent** tells you how many times the **base** is used as a factor.

Example 1 **Write 6^3 as a product of the same factor.**

The base is 6. The exponent 3 means that 6 is used as a factor 3 times.
$6^3 = 6 \cdot 6 \cdot 6$

Example 2 **Evaluate 5^4.**

$5^4 = 5 \cdot 5 \cdot 5 \cdot 5$
$\quad = 625$

Example 3 **Write $4 \cdot 4 \cdot 4 \cdot 4 \cdot 4$ in exponential form.**

The base is 4. It is used as a factor 5 times, so the exponent is 5.
$4 \cdot 4 \cdot 4 \cdot 4 \cdot 4 = 4^5$

Exercises

Write each power as a product of the same factor.

1. 7^3 **2.** 2^7 **3.** 9^2 **4.** 15^4

Evaluate each expression.

5. 3^5 **6.** 7^3 **7.** 8^4 **8.** 5^3

Write each product in exponential form.

9. $2 \cdot 2 \cdot 2 \cdot 2$ **10.** $7 \cdot 7 \cdot 7 \cdot 7 \cdot 7 \cdot 7$

11. $10 \cdot 10 \cdot 10$ **12.** $9 \cdot 9 \cdot 9 \cdot 9 \cdot 9$

13. $12 \cdot 12 \cdot 12$ **14.** $5 \cdot 5 \cdot 5 \cdot 5$

15. $6 \cdot 6 \cdot 6 \cdot 6 \cdot 6$ **16.** $1 \cdot 1 \cdot 1 \cdot 1 \cdot 1 \cdot 1 \cdot 1 \cdot 1$

1-2 Skills Practice
Powers and Exponents

Write each power as a product of the same factor.

1. 11^2 **2.** 3^4

3. 2^5 **4.** 9^3

5. 15^3 **6.** 4^3

7. 1^6 **8.** 17^4

9. 3^7 **10.** 8^6

Evaluate each expression.

11. 9^2 **12.** 8^2

13. 8^3 **14.** 2^4

15. 2^5 **16.** 6^3

17. 3^4 **18.** 3^5

19. 9^3 **20.** 11^2

21. 4^7 **22.** 12^3

23. 1^9 **24.** 10^4

25. 20^4 **26.** 2^6

Write each product in exponential form.

27. $12 \cdot 12$ **28.** $10 \cdot 10 \cdot 10$

29. $4 \cdot 4 \cdot 4 \cdot 4 \cdot 4$ **30.** $9 \cdot 9 \cdot 9 \cdot 9$

31. $15 \cdot 15 \cdot 15 \cdot 15 \cdot 15$ **32.** $6 \cdot 6 \cdot 6 \cdot 6 \cdot 6 \cdot 6 \cdot 6 \cdot 6$

Lesson 1–2

1-2 Practice

Powers and Exponents

Write each power as a product of the same factor.

1. 5^7

2. 2^4

3. 7^2

4. 10^5

5. 3^3

6. 6^8

7. *four to the eighth power*

8. *eight cubed*

9. *ten squared*

Write each product in exponential form.

10. $9 \cdot 9 \cdot 9 \cdot 9 \cdot 9 \cdot 9$

11. $1 \cdot 1 \cdot 1 \cdot 1 \cdot 1$

12. $2 \cdot 2 \cdot 2 \cdot 2 \cdot 2 \cdot 2 \cdot 2$

13. $6 \cdot 6 \cdot 6 \cdot 6 \cdot 6 \cdot 6 \cdot 6 \cdot 6 \cdot 6$

14. $5 \cdot 5$

15. $4 \cdot 4 \cdot 3 \cdot 3 \cdot 3 \cdot 3 \cdot 3$

Evaluate each expression.

16. 4^3

17. 1^{11}

18. 2^5

19. 10^3

20. 9^3

21. 8^1

22. *five to fourth power*

23. *7 squared*

24. *zero to the sixth power*

Use a calculator to determine whether each sentence is *true* or *false*.

25. $2^8 = 8^2$

26. $17^2 < 172$

27. $3^2 > 1^{19}$

Order the following powers from least to greatest.

28. $7^2, 5^3, 3^4, 2^5$

29. $4^3, 1^{13}, 12^2, 8^3$

30. $3^9, 5^7, 7^5, 9^3$

31. **INTERACTIVE MAPS** Mansi is using an interactive map on her computer that allows her to zoom in or zoom out. Each time she zooms out the scale of the map increases by a power of ten. If she zooms out four times the scale is 10^4 times greater. Write this number in standard form.

32. **BACTERIA** A lab technician observed 5 bacteria growing in a lab dish. One hour later he observed 25 bacteria. Every hour he notices about 5 times as many as the hour before. After several hours of observation, he determined the lab dish had 5^9 bacteria. Use a calculator to find the number in standard form that represents the bacteria in the lab dish.

1-2 Word Problem Practice

Powers and Exponents

---

1. SPACE SHUTTLE The cost of each flight of the Space Shuttle is about $10,000,000. Write this amount in exponential form.

2. ANIMALS The African bush elephant is the largest land animal and weighs about 8 tons. Write this amount in exponential form.

---

3. VOLUME To find the volume of a rectangular box you multiply the length times the width times the height. In a cube all sides are the same length. If the cube has length, width, and height of 6 inches, write the volume as a product. Then write it in exponential form.

4. SCIENCE A certain type of cell doubles every hour. If you start with one cell, at the end of one hour you would have 2 cells, at the end of two hours you have 4 cells, and so on. The expression $2 \times 2 \times 2 \times 2 \times 2$ tells you how many cells you would have after five hours. Write this expression in exponential form; then evaluate it.

---

5. MATH Write 625 using exponents in as many ways as you can.

6. PREFIXES Many prefixes are used in mathematics and science. The prefix giga in gigameter represents 1,000,000,000 meters. Write this prefix as a power of ten.

---

7. LIBRARY The school library contains 9^4 books. How many library books are in the school library?

8. HOT DOGS The concession stand at the county fair sold 6^3 hot dogs on the first day. How many hot dogs did they sell?

Lesson 1–2

1-2 Enrichment

The Four-Digit Problem

Use the digits 1, 2, 3, and 4 to write expressions for the numbers 1 through 50. Each digit is used exactly once in each expression. (There might be more than one expression for a given number.)

You can use addition, subtraction, multiplication (not division), exponents, and parentheses in any way you wish. Also, you can use two digits to make one number, as in 34. A few expressions are given to get you started.

$1 = (3 \times 1) - (4 - 2)$

$2 =$

$3 =$

$4 =$

$5 =$

$6 =$

$7 =$

$8 =$

$9 =$

$10 =$

$11 =$

$12 =$

$13 =$

$14 =$

$15 = 2(3 + 4) + 1$

$16 =$

$17 =$

$18 =$

$19 = 3(2 + 4) + 1$

$20 =$

$21 =$

$22 =$

$23 = 31 - (4 \times 2)$

$24 =$

$25 =$

$26 =$

$27 =$

$28 =$

$29 = 2^{(4 + 1)} - 3$

$30 =$

$31 =$

$32 =$

$33 =$

$34 =$

$35 = 2^{(4 + 1)} + 3$

$36 =$

$37 =$

$38 =$

$39 =$

$40 =$

$41 =$

$42 =$

$43 = 42 + 1^3$

$44 =$

$45 =$

$46 =$

$47 =$

$48 =$

$49 =$

$50 =$

1-2 Scientific Calculator Activity

The Power Key

The power key $\boxed{\wedge}$ on a scientific calculator makes it easier to evaluate expressions with exponents.

Example 1 Evaluate 3^5.

Enter: 3 $\boxed{\wedge}$ 5 $\boxed{\text{ENTER}}$ 243
Therefore, $3^5 = 243$.

Example 2 Evaluate $2 \cdot 4^3$.

Enter: 2 $\boxed{\times}$ 4 $\boxed{\wedge}$ 3 $\boxed{\text{ENTER}}$ 128
Therefore, $2 \cdot 4^3 = 128$.

Exercises Evaluate each expression.

1. 2^5

2. 5^4

3. 25^4

4. 10^6

5. 2^{10}

6. 9^7

7. $3 \cdot 6^3$

8. $4^3 \cdot 3^4$

9. $2^5 \cdot 5^4$

10. n^3 if $n = 5$

11. a^4 if $a = 7$

12. c^7 if $c = 4$

13. $s^2 \cdot s^5$ if $s = 3$

14. $n^3 + n^5$ if $n = 2$

15. 22 cubed

16. **CHALLENGE** What is the greatest power of 2 that the calculator will display before it gives an error message?

Lesson 1–2

1-3 Lesson Reading Guide

Squares and Square Roots

Get Ready for the Lesson

Complete the Mini Lab at the top of page 34 in your textbook.
Write your answers below.

1. Using tiles, try to construct squares with areas 4, 9, and 16 square units.

2. Try to construct squares with areas 12, 18, and 20 square units.

3. Which of the areas form squares?

4. What is the relationship between the lengths of the sides and the areas of these squares?

5. Using your square tiles, create a square that has an area of 49 square units. What are the lengths of the sides of the square?

Read the Lesson

6. In this lesson, the word *square* is used in several different ways. Tell the meaning of the word as it is used in each phrase or sentence.
   a. Find the *square* of 3.
   b. 9 units *squared*
   c. A boxing ring is a *square* with an area of 400 ft^2.

Remember What You Learned

7. Work with a partner. Use a calculator to find the squares of six numbers, some of them decimals. Then write only the squares in a list and exchange lists with your partner. Find the square roots of the squares in the list that you receive. Write your answers in the form $\sqrt{x} = y$.

1-3 Study Guide and Intervention

Squares and Square Roots

The product of a number and itself is the **square** of the number. Numbers like 4, 25, and 2.25 are called **perfect squares** because they are squares of rational numbers. The factors multiplied to form perfect squares are called **square roots**. Both $5 \cdot 5$ and $(-5)(-5)$ equal 25. So, 25 has two square roots, 5 and -5. A **radical sign**, $\sqrt{}$, is the symbol used to indicate the *positive* square root of a number. So, $\sqrt{25} = 5$.

Examples

1 Find the square of 5.

$5 \cdot 5 = 25$

2 Find the square of 16.

16 [x²] [ENTER =] **256**

3 Find $\sqrt{49}$.

$7 \cdot 7 = 49$, so $\sqrt{49} = 7$.

4 Find $\sqrt{169}$.

[2nd] [$\sqrt{}$] 169 [ENTER =] **13**

So, $\sqrt{169} = 13$.

Example 5 A square tile has an area of 144 square inches. What are the dimensions of the tile?

[2nd] [$\sqrt{}$] 144 [ENTER =] **12**   Find the square root of 144.

So, the tile measures 12 inches by 12 inches.

Exercises

Find the square of each number.

1. 2

2. 9

3. 14

4. 15

5. 21

6. 45

Find each square root.

7. $\sqrt{16}$

8. $\sqrt{36}$

9. $\sqrt{256}$

10. $\sqrt{1,024}$

11. $\sqrt{361}$

12. $\sqrt{484}$

Lesson 1–3

1-3 Skills Practice

Squares and Square Roots

Find the square of each number.

1. 3   **2.** 22

3. 25   **4.** 24

5. 35   **6.** 26

7. 37   **8.** 50

Find each square root.

9. $\sqrt{25}$ **10.** $\sqrt{100}$

11. $\sqrt{441}$ **12.** $\sqrt{900}$

13. $\sqrt{961}$ **14.** $\sqrt{784}$

15. $\sqrt{3,600}$ **16.** $\sqrt{1,936}$

17. What is the square of -37?   **18.** Find both square roots of 4,900.

19. Square 7.2.   **20.** Square 4.5.

1-3 **Practice**

Squares and Square Roots

Find the square of each number.

1. 2   **2.** 8   **3.** 10

4. 11   **5.** 15   **6.** 25

7. What is the square of 5?   **8.** Find the square of 16.   **9.** Find the square of 21.

Find each square root.

10. $\sqrt{64}$ **11.** $\sqrt{121}$ **12.** $\sqrt{169}$

13. $\sqrt{0}$ **14.** $\sqrt{81}$ **15.** $\sqrt{289}$

16. $\sqrt{900}$ **17.** $\sqrt{1}$ **18.** $\sqrt{484}$

PACKAGING An electronics company uses three different sizes of square labels to ship products to customers. The area of each type of label is shown in the table.

19. If the length of a side of a square is the square root of the area, what is the length of a side for each label?

Labels	
Type	**Area**
Priority:	100 cm^2
Caution:	225 cm^2
Address:	144 cm^2

20. How much larger is the Caution label than the Address label?

21. RECREATION A square hot tub is outlined by a 2-foot wide tile border. In an overhead view, the area of the hot tub and the border together is 144 square feet. What is the length of one side of the hot tub itself?

Lesson 1–3

1-3 Word Problem Practice

Squares and Square Roots

1. FERTILIZER John bought a bag of lawn fertilizer that will cover 400 square feet. What are the dimensions of the largest square plot of lawn that the bag of fertilizer will cover?

2. GEOMETRY The area A of a circle in square feet with a radius r in feet is given approximately by the formula $A \approx 3.14r^2$. What is the approximate area of a circle with a radius of 3 feet?

3. MOTION The time t in seconds for an object dropped from a height of h feet to hit the ground is given by the formula $t = \sqrt{\dfrac{2h}{32}}$. How long will it take an object dropped from a height of 500 feet to hit the ground? Round to the nearest tenth.

4. PACKAGING A cardboard envelope for a compact disc is a square with an area of 171.61 square centimeters. What are the dimensions of the envelope?

5. GEOGRAPHY Refer to the squares below. They represent the approximate areas of California, Alabama, and Nebraska. Find the area of Alabama.

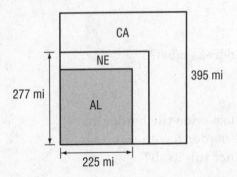

6. Use the figure in Exercise 5. How much larger is California than Nebraska?

1-3 Enrichment

The Geometric Mean

The square root of the product of two numbers is called their **geometric mean**. The geometric mean of 12 and 48 is $\sqrt{12 \cdot 48} = \sqrt{576}$ or 24.

Find the geometric mean for each pair of numbers.

1. 2 and 8

2. 4 and 9

3. 9 and 16

4. 16 and 4

5. 16 and 36

6. 12 and 3

7. 18 and 8

8. 2 and 18

9. 27 and 12

Recall the definition of a **geometric sequence**. Each term is found by multiplying the previous term by the same number. A missing term in a geometric sequence equals the geometric mean of the two terms on either side.

Find the missing term in each geometric sequence.

10. 4, 12, ⬚?⬚, 108, 324

11. 10, ⬚?⬚, 62.5, 156.25, 390.625

12. 1, 0.4, ⬚?⬚, 0.064, 0.0256

13. 700, 70, 7, 0.7, ⬚?⬚, 0.007

14. 6, ⬚?⬚, 24

15. 18, ⬚?⬚, 32

Lesson 1-3

1-3 Scientific Calculator Activity

Square Roots

Calculators have a key to square a number. This key is usually labeled $\boxed{x^2}$. Most calculators can also find the square root of a number. You may have to use the shift key to use this function.

Example 1 Find the square of 84.

Enter: 84 $\boxed{x^2}$ $\boxed{\text{ENTER}}$ 7056

$84^2 = 7,056$

Example 2 Find $\sqrt{2,025}$.

Enter: $\boxed{\text{2nd}}$ $[\sqrt{}]$ 2025 $\boxed{\text{ENTER}}$ 45

$\sqrt{2025} = 45$

Exercises

Find the square of each number.

1. 38
2. 51
3. 77

4. 101
5. 28.8
6. 15.5

7. 18.7
8. 9.9
9. 39

10. 1
11. 8.2
12. 222

Find each square root.

13. $\sqrt{900}$
14. $\sqrt{289}$
15. $\sqrt{5,184}$

16. $\sqrt{1,681}$
17. $\sqrt{5,476}$
18. $\sqrt{576}$

19. $\sqrt{1,024}$
20. $\sqrt{676}$
21. $\sqrt{2,704}$

1-4 Lesson Reading Guide
Order of Operations

Get Ready for the Lesson

Read the introduction at the top of page 38 in your textbook. Write your answers below.

1. List the differences between their calculations.

2. Whose calculations are correct?

3. Make a conjecture about what should be the first step in simplifying $6 + 4 \cdot 3$.

Read the Lesson

4. Why did mathematicians agree on an order of operations?

5. What are three ways to indicate multiplication in a mathematical expression?

Remember What You Learned

6. In your own words, describe the order of operations that is used in finding the value of a mathematical expression.

Lesson 1-4

1-4 Study Guide and Intervention

Order of Operations

Use the **order of operations** to evaluate numerical expressions.

1. Evaluate the expressions inside grouping symbols.
2. Evaluate all powers.
3. Multiply and divide in order from left to right.
4. Add and subtract in order from left to right.

Example 1 Evaluate $(10 - 2) - 4 \cdot 2$.

$$(10 - 2) - 4 \cdot 2 = 8 - 4 \cdot 2 \quad \text{Subtract first since } 10 - 2 \text{ is in parentheses.}$$
$$= 8 - 8 \quad \text{Multiply 4 and 2.}$$
$$= 0 \quad \text{Subtract 8 from 8.}$$

Example 2 Evaluate $8 + (1 + 5)^2 \div 4$.

$$8 + (1 + 5)^2 \div 4 = 8 + 6^2 \div 4 \quad \text{First, add 1 and 5 inside the parentheses.}$$
$$= 8 + 36 \div 4 \quad \text{Find the value of } 6^2.$$
$$= 8 + 9 \quad \text{Divide 36 by 4.}$$
$$= 17 \quad \text{Add 8 and 9.}$$

Exercises

Evaluate each expression.

1. $(1 + 7) \times 3$

2. $28 - 4 \cdot 7$

3. $5 + 4 \cdot 3$

4. $(40 \div 5) - 7 + 2$

5. $35 \div 7(2)$

6. 3×10^3

7. $45 \div 5 + 36 \div 4$

8. $42 \div 6 \times 2 - 9$

9. $2 \times 8 - 3^2 + 2$

10. $5 \times 2^2 + 32 \div 8$

11. $3 \times 6 - (9 - 8)^3$

12. 3.5×10^2

1-4 Skills Practice

Order of Operations

Evaluate each expression.

1. $9 - 3 + 4$

2. $8 + 6 - 5$

3. $12 \div 4 + 5$

4. $25 \times 2 - 7$

5. $36 \div 9(2)$

6. $6 + 3(7 - 2)$

7. $3 \times 6.2 + 5^2$

8. $(1 + 11)^2 \div 3$

9. $12 - (2 + 8)$

10. $15 - 24 \div 4 \cdot 2$

11. $(4 + 2) \cdot (7 + 4)$

12. $(3 \cdot 18) \div (2 \cdot 9)$

13. $24 \div 6 + 4^2$

14. $3 \times 8 - (9 - 7)^3$

15. $9 + (9 - 8 + 3)^4$

16. $3 \times 2^2 + 24 \div 8$

17. $(15 \div 3)^2 + 9 \div 3$

18. $(52 \div 4) + 5^3$

19. 26×10^3

20. 7.2×10^2

21. $5 \times 4^2 - 3 \times 2$

22. $24 \div 6 \div 2$

23. $13 - (6 - 5)^5$

24. $(8 - 3 \times 2) \times 6$

25. $(11 \cdot 4 - 10) \div 2$

26. $10 \div 2 \times (4 - 3)$

27. 1.82×10^5

28. $35 \div 7 \times 2 - 4$

29. $2^5 + 7(9 - 1)$

30. $12 + 16 \div (3 + 1)$

Lesson 1-4

1-4 Practice

Order of Operations

Evaluate each expression.

1. $(2 + 9) \times 4$

2. $8 - (5 + 2)$

3. $(15 \div 3) + 7$

4. $(14 + 7) \div 7$

5. $5 \cdot 6 - 12 \div 4$

6. $8 \div 2 + 8 - 2$

7. $16 - 8 \div 2 + 5$

8. $15 - 3 \cdot 5 + 7$

9. 7×10^3

10. $2 \times 5^2 + 6$

11. $7 \cdot 2^3 - 9$

12. $27 \div 3 \times 2 + 4^2$

13. $6^3 - 12 \times 4 \cdot 3$

14. $(15 - 3) \div (8 + 4)$

15. $(9 - 4) \cdot (7 - 7)$

16. $8 + 3(5 + 2) - 7 \cdot 2$

17. $5(6 - 1) - 4 \cdot 6 \div 3$

18. $(5 + 7)^2 \div 12$

19. $12 \div (8 - 6)^2$

20. $(7 + 2)^2 \div 3^2$

21. $(11 - 9)^2 \cdot (8 - 5)^2$

22. $64 \div 8 - 3(4 - 3) + 2$

23. $8 \times 5.1 - (4.1 + 1.4) + 7.1$

For Exercises 24 and 25, write an expression for each situation. Then evaluate the expression to find the solution.

24. LAWN AREA The Solomons need to find the area of their front and side yards since they want to reseed the lawn. Both side yards measure 3 meters by 10 meters, while the front yard is a square with a side of 9 meters. They do not need to reseed a portion of the front yard covering 16 square meters where a flower bed is located. What is the area of the yard that the Solomons want to reseed?

25. COMMUNITY SERVICE Jariah volunteers at the hospital during the week. She volunteers 3 hours on Monday and Thursday, 4 hours on Saturday and Sunday, and 2 hours on Tuesday. How many hours does Jariah volunteer at the hospital during the week?

1-4 Word Problem Practice

Order of Operations

1. **FOOTBALL** The middle school team scored three field goals worth three points each and two touchdowns with extra points worth seven points each. Write a numerical expression to find the team's score. Then evaluate the expression.

2. **BOOKS** Juan goes to the school book fair where paperback books are $1.50 and hardback books are $3.00. Juan buys 5 paperback and 2 hardback books. Write a numerical expression to find how much Juan paid for the books. Then evaluate the expression.

3. **GEOMETRY** The perimeter of a hexagon is found by adding the lengths of all six sides of the hexagon. For the hexagon below write a numerical expression to find the perimeter. Then evaluate the expression.

8
5   5
5   5
8

4. **MONEY** Aisha bought school supplies consisting of 6 spiral notebooks costing $0.39 each, 2 packages of pencils at $0.79 each, and a 3-ring binder for $1.99. Write an expression to find the total amount Aisha spent on school supplies. Then evaluate the expression.

5. **REASONING** Use the order of operations and the digits 2, 4, 6, and 8 to create an expression with a value of 2.

6. **NUMBER SENSE** Without parentheses, the expression $8 + 30 \div 2 + 4$ equals 27. Place parentheses in the expression so that it equals 13; then 23.

7. **MONEY** Tyrone bought 5 postcards at $0.55 each and a set of postcards for $1.20. Write an expression to find the total amount Tyrone spent on postcards. Then evaluate the expression.

8. **DINING** Mr. Firewalks took his family out to eat. They ordered 3 meals costing $8.99 each, 2 sodas at $1.50 each, and 1 glass of tea for $1.25. Write an expression to find the total amount the Firewalks family spent on dinner before taxes and tip. Then evaluate the expression.

Lesson 1-4

1-4 Enrichment

Nested Expressions

Nested Expressions

Sometimes more than one set of parentheses are used to group the quantities in an expression. These expressions are said to have "nested" parentheses. The expression below has "nested" parentheses.

$$(4 + (3 \cdot (2 + 3)) + 8) \div 9$$

Expressions with several sets of grouping symbols are clearer if braces such as { } or brackets such as [ ] are used. Here is the same example written with brackets and braces.

$$\{4 + [3 \cdot (2 + 3)] + 8\} \div 9$$

To evaluate expressions of this type, work from the inside out.

$$
\begin{aligned}
\{4 + [3 \cdot (2 + 3)] + 8\} \div 9 &= \{4 + [3 \cdot 5] + 8\} \div 9 \\
&= [4 + 15 + 8] \div 9 \\
&= 27 \div 9 \\
&= 3
\end{aligned}
$$

Evaluate each expression.

1. $3 + [(24 \div 8) \cdot 7] - 20$

2. $[(16 - 7 + 5) \div 2] - 7$

3. $[2 \cdot (23 - 6) + 14] \div 6$

4. $50 - [3 \cdot (15 - 5)] + 25$

5. $12 + \{28 - [2 \cdot (11 - 7)] + 3\}$

6. $\{75 + 3 \cdot [(17 - 9) \div 2]\} \cdot 2$

7. $20 + \{3 \cdot [6 + (56 \div 8)]\}$

8. $\{4 + [5 \cdot (12 - 5)] + 15\} \cdot 10$

9. $\{15 \cdot [(38 - 26) \div 4]\} - 15$

10. $\{[34 + (6 \cdot 5)] \div 8\} + 40$

1-4 TI-83/84 Plus Activity

Order of Operations

You can use a graphing calculator to evaluate expressions using the order of operations. If an expression does not have parentheses, you can enter it as you read it. The calculator will use the order of operations when finding the solution.

Example 1 $3 + 4 \cdot 5 - 6 \div 2$

Enter: 3 [+] 4 [×] 5 [−] 6 [÷] 2 [ENTER] 20

So, $3 + 4 \cdot 5 - 6 \div 2 = 20$.

If there are parentheses in the expression, you can enter them using the parentheses keys.

Example 2 $4 \cdot (3 + 2) \div (10 - 8)$

Enter: 4 [×] [( ] 3 [+] 2 [ )] [÷] [( ] 10 [−] 8 [ )] [ENTER] 10

So, $4 \cdot (3 + 2) \div (10 - 8) = 10$.

Exercises

Evaluate each expression.

1. $6 + 3 \cdot 4 - 9$

2. $4 + 28 \div 4 - 18 \div 9$

3. $6 + (5 \cdot 3)$

4. $47 - 18 + 6 \cdot (4 + 3)$

5. $3(16 - 9) + 11$

6. $24 \div (1 + 3)$

7. $5(10 - 4) + 6(56 \div 7)$

8. $6(18 - 9) - 4(3 + 2)$

Insert parentheses to make each sentence true. Check with your calculator.

9. $14 \div 2 + 5 \cdot 9 \div 3 = 6$

10. $57 - 16 - 1 \div 5 = 8$

11. $3 \cdot 16 - 12 + 4 \cdot 11 - 7 = 28$

12. $3 + 4 \div 2 + 2 - 1 = 3$

13. $4 \cdot 6 - 8 + 6 \div 2 = 17$

14. $40 + 36 \div 4 \cdot 27 - 24 = 57$

Lesson 1-4

1-5 Study Guide and Intervention

Problem-Solving Investigation: Guess and Check

When solving problems, one strategy that is helpful to use is guess and check. Based on the information in the problem, you can make a guess of the solution. Then use computations to check if your guess is correct. You can repeat this process until you find the correct solution.

You can use guess and check, along with the following four-step problem solving plan to solve a problem.

Understand	• Read and get a general understanding of the problem.
Plan	• Make a plan to solve the problem and estimate the solution.
Solve	• Use your plan to solve the problem.
Check	• Check the reasonableness of your solution.

Example

VETERINARY SCIENCE Dr. Miller saw 40 birds and cats in one day. All together the pets he saw had 110 legs. How many of each type of animal did Dr. Miller see in one day?

Understand You know that Dr. Miller saw 40 birds and cats total. You also know that there were 110 legs in all. You need to find out how many of each type of animal he saw in one day.

Plan Make a guess and check it. Adjust the guess until you get the correct answer.

Solve

Number of birds	Number of cats	Total number of feet
20	20	$2(20) + 4(20) = 120$
30	10	$2(30) + 4(10) = 100$
25	15	$2(25) + 4(15) = 110$

Check 25 birds have 50 feet. 15 cats have 60 feet. Since $50 + 60$ is 110, the answer is correct.

Exercise

GEOMETRY In a math class of 26 students, each girl drew a triangle and each boy drew a square. If there were 89 sides in all, how many girls and how many boys were in the class?

1-5

Skills Practice

Problem-Solving Investigation: Guess and Check

Solve each problem using the guess and check problem-solving strategy.

1. **SPORTS** Susan made 2-point baskets and 3-point baskets in her last basketball game. All together she scored 9 points. How many of each type of basket did she make?

2. **ENTERTAINMENT** Tickets to the local circus cost $3 for children and $5 for adults. There were three times as many children tickets sold as adult tickets. All together the circus made $700. How many children and how many adults bought tickets to the circus?

3. **NUMBERS** What are the next two numbers in the following sequence?

   5, 13, 37, 109, 325, ___, ___

4. **MONEY** Richard found $2.40 in change while cleaning his couch. He found the same number of quarters, dimes, and nickels. How many of each coin did he find?

Lesson 1-5

1-5 Practice

Problem-Solving Investigation: Guess and Check

Mixed Problem Solving

For Exercises 1 and 2, choose the appropriate method of computation. Then use the method to solve the problem.

1. **NUMBERS** A number is multiplied by 7. Then 5 is added to the product. The result is 33. What is the number?

2. **FOOD** Mr. Jones paid $23 for food for his family of seven at the ballpark. Everyone had a drink and either one hot dog or one hamburger. How many hamburgers were ordered?

MENU	
ITEM	**PRICE**
Hot Dog	$2
Hamburger	$3
Drink	$1

Use any strategy to solve Exercises 3–6. Some strategies are shown below.

PROBLEM-SOLVING STRATEGIES
• Guess and Check.
• Find a pattern.

3. **PATTERNS** What are the next two "words" in the pattern?

   ace, bdf, ceg, dfh, egi, _____ , _____

4. **GEOMETRY** The area of each square is twice the area of the next smaller square drawn in it. If the area of the smallest square is 3 square centimeters, what is the area of the largest square?

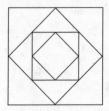

5. **ALGEBRA** What are the next two numbers in the pattern?

   32, 28, 24, 20, _____ , _____

6. **MONEY** Leeann received $60 for her birthday. The money came in $10 bills and $5 bills. If she received 8 bills, how many of each type did she receive?

7. **MONEY** Duane has four dimes, half as many nickels as dimes, and three times as many quarters as nickels. How much money does Duane have?

8. **LIBRARY** Mr. Shuck, the librarian, counted 157 books checked-in during the day. This number was 8 less than 3 times the number of books checked-out that same day. How many books were checked-out that day?

1-5 Word Problem Practice

Problem-Solving Investigation: Guess and Check

1. Joan and Amber have a combined age of 34. If Amber is 2 years less than twice Joan's age, how old is each person?

2. A number is divided by 3. Then 14 is added to the quotient. The result is 33. What is the original number?

3. The key club made $192 at their candle sale. They sold round candles for $4 and square candles for $6. If they sold twice as many square candles as round ones, how many of each type of candle did the key club sell?

4. Landon has 37 baseball cards. If 4 cards can fit on one page, how many pages does Landon need to buy?

5. Rick earns $500 less than three times as much as Jim. If their combined salary is $49,500, how much do they each earn?

6. The square root of a number is subtracted from the sum of the number and 12. The result is 42. What is the original number?

Lesson 1-5

1-6 Lesson Reading Guide

Algebra: Variables and Expressions

Get Ready for the Lesson

**Complete the Mini Lab at the top of page 44 in your textbook.
Write your answers below.**

1. Draw the next three figures in the pattern.

2. Find the number of squares in each figure and record your data in the table below. The first three are completed for you.

Figure	1	2	3	4	5	6
Number of squares	3	4	5			

3. Without drawing the figure, determine how many squares would be in the 10th figure. Check by making a drawing.

4. Find a relationship between the figure and its number of squares.

Read the Lesson

5. Match the description with the appropriate term.

The number 3 in the expression $3y + 2$. _____   **a.** variable

The entire expression $2v - 1$. _____   **b.** algebraic expression

The z in the expression $z^2 - 21$. _____   **c.** coefficient

Remember What You Learned

6. The expression $\frac{1}{3}\pi r \cdot r \cdot h$ represents the volume of a cone where r is the radius of the circular base and h is the height of the figure. Identify the coefficients, variables and constants.

1-6 Study Guide and Intervention

Algebra: Variables and Expressions

To evaluate an algebraic expression you replace each variable with its numerical value, then use the order of operations to simplify.

Example 1 Evaluate $6x - 7$ if $x = 8$.

$$
\begin{aligned}
6x - 7 &= 6(8) - 7 && \text{Replace } x \text{ with 8.} \\
&= 48 - 7 && \text{Use the order of operations.} \\
&= 41 && \text{Subtract 7 from 48.}
\end{aligned}
$$

Example 2 Evaluate $5m - 3n$ if $m = 6$ and $n = 5$.

$$
\begin{aligned}
5m - 3n &= 5(6) - 3(5) && \text{Replace } m \text{ with 6 and } n \text{ with 5.} \\
&= 30 - 15 && \text{Use the order of operations.} \\
&= 15 && \text{Subtract 15 from 30.}
\end{aligned}
$$

Example 3 Evaluate $\frac{ab}{3}$ if $a = 7$ and $b = 6$.

$$
\begin{aligned}
\frac{ab}{3} &= \frac{(7)(6)}{3} && \text{Replace } a \text{ with 7 and } b \text{ with 6.} \\
&= \frac{42}{3} && \text{The fraction bar is like a grouping symbol.} \\
&= 14 && \text{Divide.}
\end{aligned}
$$

Example 4 Evaluate $x^3 + 4$ if $x = 3$.

$$
\begin{aligned}
x^3 + 4 &= 3^3 + 4 && \text{Replace } x \text{ with 3.} \\
&= 27 + 4 && \text{Use the order of operations.} \\
&= 31 && \text{Add 27 and 4.}
\end{aligned}
$$

Exercises

Evaluate each expression if $a = 4$, $b = 2$, and $c = 7$.

1. $3ac$

2. $5b^3$

3. abc

4. $5 + 6c$

5. $\frac{ab}{8}$

6. $2a - 3b$

7. $\frac{b^4}{4}$

8. $c - a$

9. $20 - bc$

10. $2bc$

11. $ac - 3b$

12. $6a^2$

13. $7c$

14. $6a - b$

15. $ab - c$

1-6 Skills Practice

Algebra: Variables and Expressions

Evaluate each expression if $w = 2$, $x = 3$, $y = 5$, and $z = 6$.

1. $2w$

2. $y + 5$

3. $9 - z$

4. $x + w$

5. $3 + 4z$

6. $6y - 5$

7. y^2

8. $y - x$

9. $\dfrac{z}{2}$

Evaluate each expression if $m = 3$, $n = 7$, and $p = 9$.

10. $m + n$

11. $12 - 3m$

12. $5p$

13. $3.3p$

14. $3.3p + 2$

15. $2p + 3.3$

16. $20 + 2n$

17. $20 - 2n$

18. $\dfrac{n}{7}$

19. n^2

20. $6m^2$

21. $\dfrac{p^2}{3}$

22. $1.1 + n$

23. $p - 8.1$

24. $3.6m$

25. $3n - 2m$

26. $3m - n$

27. $2.1n + p$

28. $\dfrac{m^2}{p}$

29. $\dfrac{2.5m + 2.5}{5}$

30. $\dfrac{(n + 2)^2}{3}$

1-6 Practice

Algebra: Variables and Expressions

Evaluate each expression if $r = 5$, $s = 2$, $t = 7$, and $u = 1$.

1. $s + 7$ **2.** $9 - u$ **3.** $3t + 1$

4. $5r - 4$ **5.** $t - s$ **6.** $u + r$

7. $11t - 7$ **8.** $6 + 3u$ **9.** $4r - 10s$

10. $3u^2$ **11.** $2t^2 - 18$ **12.** $r^2 + 8$

13. $\dfrac{s}{2}$ **14.** $\dfrac{30}{r}$ **15.** $\dfrac{(3 + u)^2}{8}$

Evaluate each expression if $a = 4.1$, $b = 5.7$, and $c = 0.3$.

16. $a + b - c$ **17.** $10 - (a + b)$ **18.** $b - c + 2$

19. MOON The expression $\dfrac{w}{6}$ gives the weight of an object on the Moon in pounds with a weight of w pounds on Earth. What is the weight of a space suit on the Moon if the space suit weighs 178.2 pounds on Earth?

20. Complete the table.

Pounds (p)	Ounces ($16p$)
1	16
2	32
3	
4	
5	

1-6 Word Problem Practice

Algebra: Variables and Expressions

1. FIELD TRIP The seventh grade math classes are going on a field trip. The field trip will cost $7 per student. Write an expression to find the cost of the field trip for s students. What is the total cost if 26 students go on the trip?

2. SOCCER Jason earns $20 per game as a referee in youth soccer games. Write an expression to find how much money Jason will earn for refereeing any number of games. Let n represent the number of games Jason has refereed. How much will he earn for refereeing 6 games?

3. PROFIT The expressions $c - e$, where c stands for the money collected and e stands for the expenses, is used to find the profit from a basketball concession. If $500 was collected and expenses were $150, find the profit for the concession.

4. SAVINGS Kata has a savings account that contains $230. She decides to deposit $5 each month from her monthly earnings for baby-sitting after school. Write an expression to find how much money Kata will have in her savings account after x months. Let x represent the number of months. Then find out how much she will have in her account after 1 year.

5. MONEY Mr. Wilson has $2,500 in his savings account and m dollars in his checking account. Write an expression that describes the total amount that he has in both accounts.

6. ANIMALS Write an expression to represent the total number of legs on h horses and c chickens. How many legs are there in 5 horses and 6 chickens?

7. T-SHIRTS The band wants to order T-shirts. The T-shirts cost $15 each plus a shipping fee of $10. Write an expression to find the total cost of c T-shirts.

8. TEMPERATURE The expression $\frac{9}{5}C + 32$, where C stands for temperature in degrees Celsius, is used to convert Celsius to Fahrenheit. If the temperature is 20 degrees Celsius, find the temperature in degrees Fahrenheit.

1-6 Enrichment

The First Lady of Science

Chinese-American physicist Chien-Shiung Wu (1912–1997) was born in Shanghai, China. At the age of 24, she came to the United States to further her studies in science. She received her doctorate in physics from the University of California, Berkeley in 1940. Dr. Wu became the first female professor at Princeton University and worked on the Manhattan Project during World War II.

Dr. Wu paved the way for many female scientists. She received numerous awards and honors from American and Chinese universities and was the first woman president of the American Physical Society. She was also the first living scientist to have an asteroid named in her honor.

Evaluate each expression for $p = 9$, $q = 5$, $r = 7$, and $x = 8$. The problem letter and the solution form a key to decoding another fact about Dr. Wu shown below.

A. $r + 3$ **C.** $10q$ **E.** $q + r$ **G.** $p + 5$

H. $6r - x$ **N.** $6 + 4x$ **O.** $3q + 5p$ **P.** $70 - 2p$

R. $r^2 + 5$ **S.** $4q^2 - 3$ **T.** $2r^2$ **Y.** $8r - 5$

In Chinese, *Chien-Shiung* means....

___ ___ ___ ___ ___ ___   ___ ___ ___ ___
97 98 54 60 38 14   34 12 54 60

1-6 Spreadsheet Activity

Evaluating Expressions

You can use a spreadsheet to evaluate expressions.

Example 1 Evaluate $3x - 2$ when $x = -1, -2, 3,$ and 0.

Step 1 Use the first column, enter the
x values you want to substitute.
For example, enter -1 in cell A1.
Push ENTER after each value

Step 2 In cell B1, enter an equals sign
followed by the formula for the
expression which is 3*A1 − 2.
Push ENTER to get the result.
The answer is -5.

◇	A	B	C
1	-1	-5	
2	-2	-8	
3	3	7	
4	0	-2	
5			

Sheet 1

Step 3 In the second column, click on
the bottom right hand corner of cell
B1 and drag it through cell B4 to find the remaining values.

So, the values of the expression are $-5, -8, 7,$ and -2.

Example 2 Evaluate $2m + 6n$ when $m = -\frac{1}{2}$ and $n = \frac{1}{3}$.

Step 1 In cell A1, enter the
value for m. In cell B1,
enter the value for n.

Step 2 In cell C1, enter an
equals sign followed
by the formula for the
expression which is
2*A1 + 6*B1. Next
press ENTER. The answer is 1.

◇	A	B	C	D
1	-1/2	1/3	1	
2				
3				

Sheet 1

Exercises Use a spreadsheet to evaluate the following expressions
when $x = 2$.

1. $3x - 5$

2. $2x - 1$

3. $\frac{1}{2}x + 3$

4. $0.1x - 3$

5. $x + 2$

6. $5x$

Use a spreadsheet to evaluate the following expressions when $m = -1$ and $n = -2$.

7. mn

8. $\frac{n}{m}$

9. $2m + n$

10. $\frac{mn}{2}$

11. $-2m - 3n$

12. $\frac{5mn}{2}$

1-7 Lesson Reading Guide

Algebra: Equations

Get Ready for the Lesson

Read the introduction at the top of page 49 in your textbook. Write your answers below.

1. Suppose each team played 34 games. How many losses did each team have?

Women's College Volleyball		
Team	**Wins**	**Losses**
Bowling Green State University	28	
Kent State University	13	
Ohio University	28	
University of Akron	7	
University of Buffalo	14	
Miami University	13	

Source: Mid-American Conference

2. Write a rule to describe how you found the number of losses.

3. Let w represent the number of wins and ℓ represent the number of losses. Rewrite your rule using numbers, variables, and an equals sign.

Read the Lesson

4. Complete the sentence: An equation that contains a variable is neither true nor false until the variable is replaced with a _____.

5. Describe what it means to model a problem.

6. What must you do before you write an equation using a variable when modeling a problem?

Remember What You Learned

7. Calculating change after buying lunch is a situation that can be modeled with a simple equation. What other daily activities require you to solve an equation? Write down three sample equations.

1-7 Study Guide and Intervention

Algebra: Equations

- An **equation** is a sentence in mathematics that contains an equals sign, =.
- The **solution** of an equation is the value that when substituted for the variable makes the equation true.

Example 1 Solve $23 + y = 29$ mentally.

$23 + y = 29$	Write the equation.
$23 + 6 = 29$	You know that $23 + 6$ is 29.
$29 = 29$	Simplify.

The solution is 6.

Example 2

TRAVEL On their annual family vacation, the Wilsons travel 790 miles in two days. If on the first day they travel 490 miles, how many miles must they drive on the second day to reach their destination?

The total distance to travel in two days is 790 miles.

Let m represent the distance to travel on day two.

$$m + 490 = 790$$

$m + 490 = 790$	Write the equation.
$300 + 490 = 790$	Replace m with 300 to make the equation true.
$790 = 790$	Simplify.

The number 300 is the solution. The distance the Wilsons must travel on day two is 300 miles.

Exercises

Solve each equation mentally.

1. $k + 7 = 15$
2. $g - 8 = 20$
3. $6y = 24$

4. $\frac{a}{3} = 9$
5. $\frac{x}{6} = 9$
6. $8 + r = 24$

7. $12 \cdot 8 = h$
8. $n \div 11 = 8$
9. $48 \div 12 = x$

10. $h - 12 = 24$
11. $19 + y = 28$
12. $9f = 90$

Define a variable. Then write and solve an equation.

13. **MONEY** Aaron wants to buy a video game. The game costs $15.50. He has $10.00 saved from his weekly allowance. How much money does he need to borrow from his mother in order to buy the video game?

1-7 Skills Practice

Algebra: Equations

Solve each equation mentally.

1. $a + 7 = 16$

2. $12 + x = 21$

3. $4d = 60$

4. $15 = \dfrac{u}{3}$

5. $\dfrac{b}{7} = 12$

6. $13 \cdot 3 = y$

7. $8 + r = 17$

8. $27 - 12 = m$

9. $h - 22 = 67$

10. $27 + 15 = n$

11. $36 + a = 96$

12. $99 \div d = 3$

13. $6t = 66$

14. $25 = y \div 4$

15. $b - 25 = 120$

16. $n \div 5 = 10$

17. $4y = 48$

18. $5t = 40$

19. $50 \cdot d = 150$

20. $w + 61 = 65$

21. $88 \div k = 2$

Graph the solution of each equation on a number line.

22. $v - 6 = 30$

23. $3a = 27$

24. $n + 7 = 14$

Define a variable. Write an equation and solve.

25. BAKING Judy wants to buy some cookies for her birthday party. Cookies come in packages of 6. If she is inviting 24 friends to her party, how many packages of cookies does she need to buy so that each of her friends can have one cookie each?

1-7 Practice

Algebra: Equations

Solve each equation mentally.

1. $a + 5 = 14$

2. $7 + y = 24$

3. $t - 13 = 33$

4. $b - 17 = 11$

5. $12 - r = 0$

6. $x + 18 = 59$

7. $63 = 9g$

8. $8d = 96$

9. $n = \dfrac{42}{7}$

10. $9 = \dfrac{z}{7}$

11. $10 = h \div 4$

12. $55 \div m = 11$

13. $1.2 + k = 3.0$

14. $2.7 = f - 1.1$

15. $v - 0.5 = 0.2$

16. $12.6 - c = 7.0$

17. $8.8 + j = 18.7$

18. $w + 13.5 = 16.0$

19. **WEATHER** The temperature was 78°F. A cold front moved in, and the temperature dropped to 54°F. Solve the equation $78 - d = 54$ to find the drop in temperature.

20. **HOBBIES** Elissa can cut out the pieces of cloth to make four pillows in one hour. Solve the equation $4h = 20$ to find how many hours Elissa needs to cut cloth for 20 pillows.

21. **BOWLING** Jean Conrad is an amateur bowler with an average score of 187. She recently bowled a perfect 300 score. Write an equation that can be used to find how much the perfect score was above her average score and then solve the equation.

1-7 Word Problem Practice

Algebra: Equations

Lesson 1-7

1. **GAS MILEAGE** Mr. Moseley's car has a 20-gallon gas tank. It took 14 gallons of gas to fill his tank. Use the equation $14 + g = 20$ to find the number of gallons g that he had before he filled his tank with gas.

2. **PAINTING** Latisha earned $5 an hour painting for her dad. If she made $40 last week, use $5h = 40$ to find how many hours h she painted.

3. **LUMBER** Mrs. Garcia had a piece of board that was 15 feet long. She cut off 6.5 feet. Use the equation $6.5 + \ell = 15$ to determine how much of the board ℓ she has left.

4. **MAGAZINES** Mahpee was selling magazine subscriptions. He earned $5 plus $0.50 for each subscription he sold. If Mahpee earned $25, use the equation $25 = 5 + 0.50n$ to find the number of subscriptions n he sold.

5. **TIRES** The cost of a car tire is $45 plus $10 per order regardless of the number of tires purchased. If Mrs. Sato places an order for $190, use the equation $45t + 10 = 190$ to find the number of tires t she purchased.

6. **AREA** If the area of a rectangle is 30 square centimeters and the length is 6 centimeters, use the equation $30 = 6w$ to find the width w of the rectangle.

7. **SUPPLIES** The Jones Middle School had $4,000 to spend on office supplies. They had already spent $1,250. Use the equation $1,250 + d = 4,000$ to find how much money d the school had left for other supplies.

8. **PENCILS** Mi-Leng spent 90 cents on 6 pencils. Use the equation $90 = 6c$ to find the cost c of each pencil.

1-7 Enrichment

Equations as Models

Equations as Models

When you write an equation that represents the information in a problem, the equation serves as a model for the problem. One equation can be a model for several different problems.

Each of Exercises 1–8 can be modeled by one of these equations.

$$n + 2 = 10 \qquad n - 2 = 10 \qquad 2n = 10 \qquad \frac{n}{2} = 10$$

Choose the correct equation. Then solve the problem.

1. Chum earned $10 for working two hours. How much did he earn per hour?

2. Ana needs $2 more to buy a $10 scarf. How much money does she already have?

3. Kathy and her brother won a contest and shared the prize equally. Each received $10. What was the amount of the prize?

4. Jameel loaned two tapes to a friend. He has ten tapes left. How many tapes did Jameel originally have?

5. In the figure below, the length of $\overline{AC}$ is 10 cm. The length of $\overline{BC}$ is 2 cm. What is the length of $\overline{AB}$?

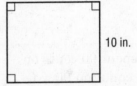

6. Ray $\overline{AC}$ bisects $\angle BAD$. The measure of $\angle BAC$ is 10°. What is the measure of $\angle BAD$?

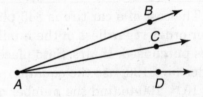

7. The width of the rectangle below is 2 inches less than the length. What is the length?

10 in.

8. In the triangle below, the length of $\overline{PQ}$ is twice the length of $\overline{QR}$. What is the length of $\overline{QR}$?

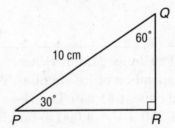

9. **CHALLENGE** On a separate sheet of paper, write a problem that can be modeled by the equation $3a + 5 = 29$.

1-8 Lesson Reading Guide

Algebra: Properties

Get Ready for the Lesson

Read the introduction at the top of page 53 in your textbook. Write your answers below.

1. Find the total cost of admission and a movie ticket for a 4-person family.

2. Describe the method you used to find the total cost.

Read the Lesson

3. Describe what is meant by *equivalent expressions*.

4. The Identity Property says that adding _____ to a number results in the number and multiplying _____ by a number is the number.

Remember What You Learned

5. Why are the Distributive Property, Commutative Property, Associative Property, and Identity Property called properties?

   Use a dictionary to find the meanings of *distribute* and *commute* that apply to mathematics. Then write an explanation of why the Distributive Property and Commutative Property are named that way.

Lesson 1-8

1-8 Study Guide and Intervention

Algebra: Properties

Property	Arithmetic	Algebra
Distributive Property	$5(3 + 4) = 5(3) + 5(4)$	$a(b + c) = a(b) + a(c)$
Commutative Property of Addition	$5 + 3 = 3 + 5$	$a + b = b + a$
Commutative Property of Multiplication	$5 \times 3 = 3 \times 5$	$a \times b = b \times a$
Associative Property of Addition	$(2 + 3) + 4 = 2 + (3 + 4)$	$(a + b) + c = a + (b + c)$
Associative Property of Multiplication	$(4 \times 5) \times 6 = 4 \times (5 \times 6)$	$(a \times b) \times c = a \times (b \times c)$
Identity Property of Addition	$5 + 0 = 5$	$a + 0 = a$
Identity Property of Multiplication	$5 \times 1 = 5$	$a \times 1 = a$

Example 1 Use the Distributive Property to write $6(4 + 3)$ as an equivalent expression. Then evaluate the expression.

$$6(4 + 3) = 6 \cdot 4 + 6 \cdot 3 \qquad \text{Apply the Distributive Property.}$$
$$= 24 + 18 \qquad \text{Multiply.}$$
$$= 42 \qquad \text{Add.}$$

Example 2 Name the property shown by each statement.

$5 \times 4 = 4 \times 5$ Commutative Property of Multiplication

$12 + 0 = 12$ Identity Property of Addition

$7 + (6 + 3) = (7 + 6) + 3$ Associative Property of Addition

Exercises

Use the Distributive Property to write each expression as an equivalent expression. Then evaluate the expression.

1. $5(7 + 2)$ 2. $4(9 + 1)$ 3. $2(6 + 7)$

Name the property shown by each statement.

4. $9 \times 1 = 9$ 5. $7 \times 3 = 3 \times 7$

6. $(7 + 8) + 2 = 7 + (8 + 2)$ 7. $6(3 + 2) = 6(3) + 6(2)$

8. $15 + 12 = 12 + 15$ 9. $1 \times 20 = 20$

10. $(9 \times 5) \times 2 = 9 \times (5 \times 2)$ 11. $3 = 0 + 3$

1-8 Skills Practice

Algebra: Properties

Use the Distributive Property to write each expression as an equivalent expression. Then evaluate the expression.

1. $3(5 + 1)$

2. $(2 + 7)5$

3. $(10 + 2)7$

4. $2(9 - 8)$

5. $4(10 - 2)$

6. $6(13 + 4)$

Name the property shown by each statement.

7. $2 \times (3 \times 7) = (2 \times 3) \times 7$

8. $6 + 3 = 3 + 6$

9. $3(9 - 7) = 3(9) - 3(7)$

10. $18 \times 1 = 18$

11. $7 \times 2 = 2 \times 7$

12. $6 + (1 + 4) = (6 + 1) + 4$

13. $7 + 0 = 7$

14. $0 + 12 = 12$

15. $625 + 281 = 281 + 625$

16. $(12 \times 18) \times 5 = 12 \times (18 \times 5)$

17. $2(8 + 2) = 2(8) + 2(2)$

18. $(15 + 11) + 9 = 15 + (11 + 9)$

19. $(6 + r) + s = 6 + (r + s)$

20. $(4 \times 8) \times a = 4 \times (8 \times a)$

21. $p \times 1 = p$

22. $a + 5 = 5 + a$

23. $y \times 3 = 3 \times y$

24. $b + 0 = b$

25. $(x + y) + z = x + (y + z)$

26. $6(200 + 50) = 6(200) + 6(50)$

Lesson 1–8

1-8 Practice

Algebra: Properties

Use the Distributive Property to evaluate each expression.

1. $4(5 + 7)$

2. $6(3 + 1)$

3. $(10 + 8)2$

4. $5(8 - 3)$

5. $7(4 - 1)$

6. $(9 - 2)3$

Name the property shown by each statement.

7. $7 + (6 + t) = (7 + 6) + t$

8. $23 \cdot 15 = 15 \cdot 23$

9. $0 + x = x$

10. $3(g + 7) = 3 \cdot g + 3 \cdot 7$

11. $8 \times 1 = 8$

12. $y + 11 = 11 + y$

13. $5(w + 1) = (w + 1)5$

14. $(4 \cdot d) \cdot 1 = 4 \cdot (d \cdot 1)$

15. $(6 + 2)7 = (6)7 + (2)7$

Use one or more properties to rewrite each expression as an equivalent expression that does not use parentheses.

16. $(b + 3) + 6$

17. $7(5x)$

18. $4(a + 4)$

19. $7 + (3 + t)$

20. $(2z)0$

21. $(9 + k)5$

22. $8(y - 5) + y$

23. $(h + 2)3 - 2h$

24. GROCERY A grocery store sells an imported specialty cheesecake for $11 and its own store-baked cheesecake for $5. Use the Distributive Property to mentally find the total cost for 6 of each type of cheesecake.

25. CHECKING ACCOUNT Mr. Kenrick balances his checking account statement each month two different ways as shown by the equation, $(b + d) - c = b + (d - c)$, where b is the previous balance, d is the amount of deposits made, and c is the amount of checks written. Name the property that Mr. Kenrick uses to double check his arithmetic.

26. SPEED A train is traveling at a speed of 65 miles per hour. The train travels for one hour. What property is used to solve this problem as shown by the statement $65 \cdot 1 = 65$?

1-8 Word Problem Practice

Algebra: Properties

1. MUSIC Mr. Escalante and Mrs. Turner plan to take their music classes to a musical revue. Tickets cost $6 each. Mr. Escalante's class needs 22 tickets, and Mrs. Turner's class needs 26 tickets. Use the Distributive Property to write a sentence to express how to find the total cost of tickets in two ways.

2. SAVINGS Mrs. Perez was looking at her bank account statement. She noticed that her beginning balance was $500, and she had added nothing to her account. What was the ending balance on her statement? What property did you apply?

3. ADDITION Mr. Brooks was working on addition using dominos with a group of 1st graders. When picking the domino with 3 dots on one end and 5 dots on the other, some students read. "3 plus 5 equal 8" while others read it as "5 plus 3 equals 8." What property were these children using? Explain.

4. AREA Aleta noticed that for the rectangle below she could either multiply 2 times 3 or 3 times 2 to get its area of 6 square inches. What property allows her to do this?

3 in.

2 in.

5. NUMBER CUBES Students in Mr. Rivas' class were practicing their multiplication skills by rolling three 6-sided number cubes. Wapi rolled a 2, a 3, and a 5 on his roll. He multiplied the three numbers as follows using the order of operations: $(2 \times 3) \times 5 = 30$. Write another way Wapi could have performed the multiplication without changing the order of the numbers. State the property you used.

6. FACTS Bik was working on memorizing her multiplication facts. She noticed that anytime she multiplied a number by 1, she got the same number she started with. What property allows this to be true?

7. MONEY Mei was trying to figure out the cost of 4 boxes of cereal for $2.25 each. Write a sentence to show Mei an easy way to do her calculations. What property did you apply to help her?

8. WALKING Jacob walked 3 blocks to Ping's house, then 5 blocks to Jamal's house. Write a sentence to show that the distance from Ping's to Jamal's is the same as the return walk home. Name the property illustrated in your sentence.

Lesson 1-8

1-8 Enrichment

Name That Property

Name That Property

You know that the Commutative Property applies to the operations of addition and multiplication. You also know that the Associative Property applies to operations of addition and multiplication. What about the other operations? Does the Commutative Property apply to division? Does the Associative Property apply to subtraction? Does the Distributive Property apply to subtraction or division?

Look at these examples to determine if the properties also apply to subtraction or division.

Commutative Property

Subtraction
Try this:
$$5 - 4 \stackrel{?}{=} 4 - 5$$

Division
Try this:
$$8 \div 2 \stackrel{?}{=} 2 \div 8$$

1. Does the Commutative Property apply to division and subtraction? Explain.

Associative Property

Subtraction
Try this:
$$7 - (3 - 2) \stackrel{?}{=} (7 - 3) - 2$$

Division
Try this:
$$8 \div (4 \div 2) \stackrel{?}{=} (8 \div 4) \div 2$$

2. Does the Associative Property apply to subtraction and division? Explain.

Distributive Property

Subtraction
Try this:
$$3(8 - 2) \stackrel{?}{=} 3 \times 8 - 3 \times 2$$
$$3(6) \stackrel{?}{=} 24 - 6$$
$$18 = 18 \checkmark$$

Division
Try this:
$$3(8 \div 2) \stackrel{?}{=} 3 \times 8 \div 3 \times 2$$
$$3(4) \stackrel{?}{=} 24 \div 6$$
$$12 \neq 4$$

3. Does the Distributive Property apply to multiplication over subtraction? Does it apply to multiplication over division? Explain.

1-8 Scientific Calculator Activity

The Distributive Property

You can solve word problems by using the Distributive Property. The parentheses keys on the calculator will help you.

Example 1　Neil purchased 4 dozen blueberry bagels and 6 dozen cinnamon-raisin bagels for a fund-raiser at school. How many bagels did Neil purchase in all?

Enter: 12 ☒ 〔(4 ＋ 6 〕) $\begin{smallmatrix}\text{ENTER}\\=\end{smallmatrix}$ 120

Neil purchased 120 bagels in all.

Example 2　Jill has been training to run a marathon for 3 weeks. On the first 7 days, she ran 2.5 miles per day. On the next 7 days, she ran 3 miles each day. On each of the last 7 days, she ran 3.75 miles. How many miles in all did Jill run?

Enter: 7 ☒ 〔(2.5 ＋ 3 ＋ 3.75 〕) $\begin{smallmatrix}\text{ENTER}\\=\end{smallmatrix}$ 64.75

Jill ran 64.75 miles during 3 weeks of training.

Exercises

Solve each problem using the Distributive Property.

1. The company assistant put in an order for supplies that included 15 dozen pens and 8 dozen pencils. How many individual pens and pencils were ordered in all?

2. The Music Source is having a sale on CDs and cassettes. They have 140 CDs and 215 cassettes they are selling for $5.29 each. How much money will they earn if all CDs and cassettes are sold?

3. If the Music Source decreased the selling price to $4.95, how much money would they earn? What is the difference in earnings from Exercise 2?

4. Kevin earns $3.15 per hour for each hour he helps Mr. McCready with lawn work. Kevin worked the following hours: Friday: 3.25 hours; Saturday: 4 hours; Sunday: 2.5 hours. How much money did Kevin earn in all? Round to the nearest cent.

Lesson 1-8

1-9 Lesson Reading Guide

Algebra: Arithmetic Sequences

Get Ready for the Lesson

Complete the Mini Lab at the top of page 57 in your textbook.
Write your answers below.

1. How many centimeter cubes are used to make each figure?

2. What pattern do you see? Describe it in words.

3. Suppose this pattern continues. Complete the table to find the number of cubes needed to make each figure.

Figure	1	2	3	4	5	6	7	8
Cubes Needed	4	8	12					

4. How many cubes would you need to make the 10th figure? Explain your reasoning.

Read the Lesson

Complete each sentence.

5. In an arithmetic sequence, each term is found by _____ the same number to the previous term.

6. In a geometric sequence, each term is found by _____ the previous term by the same number.

What is the next term in each of the following sequences?

7. 1, 5, 25, …
$\underset{\times 5 \ \times 5}{\smile\ \smile}$

8. 7, 10, 13, …
$\underset{+3 \ +3}{\smile\ \smile}$

Remember What You Learned

9. Write down the first four terms of two of your own sequences, an arithmetic sequence and a geometric sequence. Trade with a partner. Describe your partner's sequences. How did you identify the patterns?

1-9 Study Guide and Intervention

Algebra: Arithmetic Sequences

An **arithmetic sequence** is a list in which each term is found by adding the same number to the previous term. 1, 3, 5, 7, 9, …
+2 +2 +2 +2

Example 1 Describe the relationship between terms in the arithmetic sequence 17, 23, 29, 35, … Then write the next three terms in the sequence.

17, 23, 29, 35, ….   Each term is found by adding 6 to the previous term.
+6 +6 +6 $35 + 6 = 41$ $41 + 6 = 47$ $47 + 6 = 53$

The next three terms are 41, 47, and 53.

Example 2

MONEY Brian's parents have decided to start giving him a monthly allowance for one year. Each month they will increase his allowance by $10. Suppose this pattern continues. What algebraic expression can be used to find Brian's allowance after any given number of months? How much money will Brian receive for allowance for the 10th month?

Make a table to display the sequence.

Position	Operation	Value of Term
1	$1 \cdot 10$	10
2	$2 \cdot 10$	20
3	$3 \cdot 10$	30
n	$n \cdot 10$	$10n$

Each term is 20 times its position number. So, the expression is $10n$.
How much money will Brian earn after 10 months?
$10n$ Write the expression.
$10(10) = 100$ Replace n with 10

So, for the 10th month Brian will receive $100.

Exercises

Describe the relationship between terms in the arithmetic sequences. Write the next three terms in the sequence.

1. 2, 4, 6, 8, …   **2.** 4, 7, 10, 13, …   **3.** 0.3, 0.6, 0.9, 1.2, …

4. 200, 212, 224, 236, …   **5.** 1.5, 2.0, 2.5, 3.0, …   **6.** 12, 19, 26, 33, …

7. SALES Mama's bakery just opened and is currently selling only two types of pastry. Each month, Mama's bakery will add two more types of pastry to their menu. Suppose this pattern continues. What algebraic expression can be used to find the number of pastries offered after any given number of months? How many pastries will be offered in one year?

Lesson 1-9

1-9 Skills Practice

Algebra: Arithmetic Sequences

Describe the relationship between the terms in each arithmetic sequence.

1. 3, 6, 9, 12...

2. 1, 3, 5, 7, ...

3. 1, 2, 3, 4, ...

4. 0, 7, 14, 21, ...

5. 2, 5, 8, 11, ...

6. 5, 10, 15, 20, ...

7. 0.3, 0.6, 0.9, 1.2, ...

8. 1, 10, 19, 28, ...

9. 6, 18, 24, 30, ...

10. 0.5, 2.5, 4.5, 6.5, ...

11. 3, 7, 11, 15, ...

12. 0, 4.5, 9, 13.5, ...

13. 11, 22, 33, 44, ...

14. 11, 22, 33, 44, ...

Give the next three terms in each sequence.

15. 3, 6, 9, 12, ...

16. 18, 21, 24, 27, ...

17. 7, 10, 13, 16, ...

18. 4, 8, 12, 16, ...

19. 0, 7, 14, 21, ...

20. 7, 12, 17, 22, ...

21. 5, 7, 9, 11, ...

22. 5, 15, 25, 35, ...

23. 21, 42, 63, 84, ...

24. 1.1, 2.2, 3.3, 4.4, ...

25. 0.5, 1.0, 1.5, 2.0, ...

26. 1.7, 1.9, 2.1, 2.3, ...

27. 0.5, 1.5, 2.5, 3.5, ...

28. 0.1, 0.2, 0.3, 0.4, ...

1-9 **Practice**

Algebra: Arithmetic Sequences

Describe the relationship between the terms in each arithmetic sequence. Then write the next three terms in each sequence.

1. 0, 5, 10, 15, …   **2.** 1, 3, 5, 7, …   **3.** 18, 27, 36, 45, …

4. 7, 19, 31, 43, …   **5.** 8, 18, 28, 38, …   **6.** 25, 26, 27, 28, …

7. 0.4, 0.8, 1.2, 1.6, …   **8.** 3.7, 3.7, 3.7, 3.7, …   **9.** 5.1, 6.2, 7.3, 8.4, …

10. 17, 31, 45, 59, …   **11.** 30, 50, 70, 90, …   **12.** 14, 41, 68, 95, …

In a *geometric sequence*, each term is found by multiplying the previous term by the same number. Write the next three terms of each geometric sequence.

13. 5, 10, 20, 40, …   **14.** 3, 9, 27, 81, …   **15.** 2, 8, 32, 128, …

NUMBER SENSE   **Find the 40th term in each arithmetic sequence.**

16. 4, 8, 12, 16, …   17. 13, 26, 39, 52, …   **18.** 6, 12, 18, 24, …

19. GEOMETRY   The lengths of the sides of a 6-sided polygon are in arithmetic sequence. The length of the shortest side is 3 meters. If the length of the next longer side is 5 meters, what is the length of the longest side?

20. FREE FALLING OBJECT   A free falling object increases speed by a little over 22 miles per hour each second. The arithmetic sequence 22, 44, 66, …, represents the speed after each second, in miles per hour, of a dropped object. How fast is a rock falling after 8 seconds if it is dropped over the side of a cliff?

Lesson 1-9

1-9 Word Problem Practice

Algebra: Arithmetic Sequences

---

1. NUMBERS The multiples of two form a sequence as follows: 2, 4, 6, 8, 10, 12, 14, 16, …. Describe the sequence you see? What about the multiples of three? Four? Five?

2. OLYMPICS The summer Olympics occur every four years. If the last summer Olympics happened in 2004, when are the next three times that it will occur? Describe the sequence the Olympic years form?

---

3. BABY-SITTING Tonya charges $3.50 per hour to baby-sit. The sequence $3.50, $7.00, $10.50, $14.00, … represents how much she charges for each subsequent hour. For example, $10.50 is the third term that represents how much she charges for 3 hours. What are the next three terms in the sequence? How much does she charge for 7 hours of baby-sitting?

4. RECTANGLES Suppose you start with 1 rectangle and then divide it in half. You now have 2 rectangles. You divide each of these in half, and you have 4 rectangles. The sequence for this division is 1, 2, 4, 8, 16, . . . rectangles after each successive division. Describe the sequence that results?

---

5. BACTERIA Three bacteria are in a dish. Each hour the number of bacteria multiplies by four. If at the end of the first hour there are 12 bacteria, how many bacteria are there at the end of the next three hours? Describe the sequence that results?

6. ENROLLMENT The enrollment at Grove Middle School is expected to increase by 40 students each year for the next 5 years. If their current enrollment is 600 students, find their enrollment after each of the next 5 years.

---

7. SALARY Mrs. Malone's current salary is $1,500. She expects it to increase $100 per year. Write the first 6 terms of a sequence that represents her salary. The first term should be her current salary. What does the sixth term represent?

8. FIBONACCI The Fibonacci sequence is named after Leonardo Fibonacci who first explored it. Look at the Fibonacci sequence below and describe its pattern. 1, 1, 2, 3, 5, 8, 13, 21, 34, …

1-9 Enrichment

Other Sequences

When each term in a sequence decreases, it is described as a *declining sequence*. Either subtracting the same number from the previous term or dividing the previous term by the same number creates a declining sequence.

$$81, 27, 9, 3, \ldots$$
$$\div 3 \ \div 3 \ \div 3$$

> In this sequence, each term is found by dividing the previous term by 3.

Some sequences are formed by using two operations.

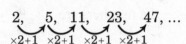

$$2, \quad 5, \quad 11, \quad 23, \quad 47, \ldots$$
$$\times 2+1 \ \times 2+1 \ \times 2+1 \ \times 2+1$$

> In this sequence, each term is found by multiplying the previous term by 2 and then adding 1.

Describe the rule in each sequence. Then write the next three terms.

1. 40, 38, 36, 34, …

2. 128, 64, 32, 16, …

3. 7.5, 6.4, 5.3, 4.2, …

4. 1, 4, 13, 40, …

5. 1, 5, 13, 61, …

6. 1, 5, 21, 85, …

Create a five-term sequence using the rule stated. Start with the given number.

7. Subtract 8 from each term; 78.

8. Divide each term by 10; 80.

9. Subtract 11 from each term; 132.

10. Multiply each term by 10 and subtract 9; 4.

11. Multiply each term by 7 and add 2; 1.

12. Multiply each term by 3 and subtract 2; 6.

CHALLENGE For Exercises 13–15, use the sequence 589, 5,889, 58,889, 588,889, …

13. Describe the rule of the sequence.

14. Study the pattern in the sequence. Without extending the sequence, what is the sixth term of the sequence? What is the tenth term?

15. Describe how you can find any term of the sequence.

Lesson 1-9

1-9 Scientific Calculator Activity

Geometric Sequences

A **geometric sequence** is a list in which each term is found by *multiplying* the previous term by the same number. 2, 6, 18, 54, ...

× 3 × 3 × 3

• • •   • • •   • • • • • •   • • • • • • • • • • • •
• • •   • • • • • •   • • • • • • • • • • • •

$n = 3$ $n = 6$ $n = 12$ $n = 24$

Look for a pattern in the groups of dots above. Can you see that each time the number of dots doubles? The number of dots in each group forms the *geometric sequence* 3, 6, 12, 24. In a geometric sequence, the numbers are related by multiplication.

Example   **Find the next three numbers in the geometric sequence: 0.8, 2.4, 7.2, 21.6.**

Divide the second term by the first term to find the *common ratio*.

Enter: 2.4 ÷ 0.8 **ENTER =** 3

Multiply the last term by the common ratio to find the next term.

Enter: 21.6 × 3 **ENTER =** 64.8

Repeat the last step until you get all of the terms.

Enter: 64.8 × 3 **ENTER =** 194.4

Enter: 194.4 × 3 **ENTER =** 583.2

The next three terms are 64.8, 194.4, and 583.2.

Exercises

Find the next three terms in each geometric sequence.

1. 0.1, 0.01, 0.001   **2.** 8, 1.6, 0.32   **3.** 12, 54, 243

4. 18, 27, 40.5   **5.** 2.1, 0.42, 0.084   **6.** 256, 128, 64

7. 0.05, 0.1, 0.2   **8.** 8.4, 0.84, 0.084   **9.** 9, 31.5, 110.25

1-10 Lesson Reading Guide

Algebra: Equations and Functions

Get Ready for the Lesson

Read the introduction at the top of page 63 in your textbook. Write your answers below.

1. Complete the table to find the cost of 2, 3, and 4 magazines.

Magazines		
Number	**Multiply by 4**	**Cost($)**
1	4×1	4
2		
3		
4		

2. Describe the pattern in the table between the cost and the number of magazines.

Read the Lesson

3. Complete each function table. Then identify the domain and range.

a.

x	$2x - 1$	y
-1		
0		
1		

b.

x	$4x$	y
-1		
0		
1		

4. **MONEY** John earns $15 per lawn that he mows.

   a. Write an equation in two variables showing the relationship between lawns mowed and the money John earns.

   b. How much money does John earn after mowing 3, 5, and 10 lawns?

Remember What You Learned

5. Draw a picture of a "machine" that shows how a function works. Your picture should illustrate input, a function rule, and output.

Lesson 1–10

1-10 Study Guide and Intervention

Algebra: Equations and Functions

The solution of an equation with two variables consists of two numbers, one for each variable that makes the equation true. When a relationship assigns exactly one output value for each input value, it is called a function. Function tables help to organize input numbers, output numbers, and function rules.

Example 1 **Complete a function table for $y = 5x$. Then state the domain and range.**

Choose four values for x. Substitute the values for x into the expression. Then evaluate to find the y value.

x	$5x$	y
0	5(0)	0
1	5(1)	5
2	5(2)	10
3	5(3)	15

The domain is {0, 1, 2, 3}. The range is {0, 5, 10, 15}.

Exercises

Complete the following function tables. Then state the domain and range.

1. $y = x + 4$

x	$x + 4$	y
0		
1		
2		
3		

2. $y = 10x$

x	$10x$	y
1		
2		
3		
4		

3. $y = x - 1$

x	$x - 1$	y
2		
3		
4		
5		

4. $y = 3x$

x	$3x$	y
10		
11		
12		
13		

1-10 Skills Practice

Algebra: Equations and Functions

Copy and complete each function table. Identify the domain and range.

1. $y = x - 1$

x	$x - 1$	y
1		
2		
3		
4		

2. $y = x + 7$

x	$x + 7$	y
1		
2		
3		
4		

3. $y = 3x$

x	$3x$	y
1		
2		
3		
4		

4. $y = 4x$

x	$4x$	y
2		
3		
4		
5		

5. $y = x - 0.5$

x	$x - 0.5$	y
1		
2		
3		
4		

6. $y = 10x$

x	$10x$	y
0		
1		
2		
3		

Solve each word problem.

For Exercises 7 and 8, use the following information.

TRAVEL For every gallon of gas, a car can travel 30 miles.

7. Write an equation using two variables to show the relationship between the distance the car travels and the gallons of gas it uses.

8. If a car had 8 gallons of gas left in its tank, how many miles can it travel before the tank runs out?

For Exercises 9 and 10, use the following information.

FARMING Every row of corn in Mr. Jones' garden has 5 cornstalks.

9. Write an equation using two variables to show the relationship between the number of rows and the number of cornstalks.

10. If Mr. Jones has 7 rows of corn, how many cornstalks will he need to harvest?

Lesson 1-10

1-10 Practice

Algebra: Equations and Functions

Complete each function table. Then identify the domain and range.

1. $y = 5x$

x	5x	y
1		
2		
3		
4		

2. $y = 8x$

x	8x	y
1		
2		
3		
4		

3. $y = 7x$

x	7x	y
3		
4		
5		
6		

4. $y = x - 2$

x	x − 2	y
2		
3		
4		
5		

5. $y = x + 3$

x	x + 3	y
2		
3		
4		
5		

6. $y = x + 0.75$

x	x + 0.75	y
0		
1		
2		
3		

7. PRODUCTION A car manufacturer makes 15,000 hybrid cars a month. Using the function table, find the number of hybrid cars produced after 3, 6, 9, and 12 months.

m	15,000m	P
3		
6		
9		
12		

8. SUNSPOTS The changing activity of sunspots, which are cooler and darker areas of the sun, occur in 11-year cycles. Use the function $y = 11c$ to find the numbers of years necessary to complete 1, 2, 3, and 4 sunspot cycles.

1-10 Word Problem Practice

Algebra: Equations and Functions

1. TECHNOLOGY The fee for your pager service is $22 per month. Make a function table that shows your total charge for 1, 2, 3, and 4 months of service.

2. MEASUREMENT Joe takes 2 steps for every one step that Kim takes. Write an equation in two variables showing the relationship between Joe's steps and Kim's steps. If Kim takes 15 steps, how many steps will Joe have to take to cover the same distance?

3. TRAINS Between Hiroshima and Kokura, Japan, the bullet train averages a speed of 164 miles per hour, which is the fastest scheduled train service in the world. Make a function table that shows the distance traveled at that speed in 1, 2, 3, and 4 hours.

4. BUSINESS Grant earns $5 for each magazine that he sells. Write an equation in two variables showing the relationship between the number of magazines sold and the amount of money made. If Grant sells 12 magazines, how much money will he make?

5. GEOMETRY The formula for the volume of a rectangular prism whose base has an area of 8 square units is $V = 8h$, where V is the volume and h is the height. Make a function table that shows the volume of a rectangular prism with a height of 3, 4, 5, and 6 units.

6. GEOMETRY The fastest insect in the world is the dragonfly with a top speed of 36 miles per hour. Write an equation in two variables describing the relationship between the length of the dragonfly's flight and the distance traveled. If a dragonfly flies for 3 hours, how far can he travel?

Lesson 1-10

1-10 Enrichment

To solve equations containing two variables, find ordered pair solutions for the equation by selecting values for x and completing a table. Although any value can be selected for x, values usually selected include $-2, -1, 0, 1,$ and 2.

For example, to solve the equation $y = 2x$ given below in Exercise 1, first select values for x, then complete a table.

Ordered pair solutions for the equation $y = 2x$ include $(-2, -4)$, $(-1, -2)$, $(0, 0)$, $(1, 2)$, and $(2, 4)$.

Match each equation with the point whose coordinates are a solution of the equation. Then, at the bottom of the page, write the letter of the point on the line directly above the number of the equation *each time it appears*. (The first one has been done as an example.) If you have matched the equations and solutions correctly, the letters below will reveal a message.

1. $y = 2x$	$A(-3, 8)$	$N(-1, 0)$
2. $y = x - 3$	$B(0, 2)$	$O(3, 0)$
3. $y = -x + 1$	$C(-2, 1)$	$P(1, 5)$
4. $y = 3x - 2$	$D(0, -5)$	$Q(0, 6)$
5. $y = -2x - 4$	$E(-1, -5)$	$R(1, 6)$
6. $y = x + (-2)$	$F(1, 3)$	$S(2, 1)$
7. $y = -4x - 1$	$G(0, -4)$	$T(-2, 3)$
8. $y = \frac{1}{2}x$	$H(-1, 3)$	$U(1, 2)$
9. $y = x + 3$	$I(2, 0)$	$V(-3, 5)$
10. $y = 7x + 7$	$J(0, 4)$	$W(0, -7)$
11. $y = -2x - 6$	$K(-3, 1)$	$X(-3, -3)$
12. $y = -x + 5$	$L(-4, 2)$	$Y(1, 8)$
13. $y = -5x + 8$	$M(-2, 2)$	$Z(0, -8)$
14. $y = -x$		

‾‾ ‾‾ ‾‾ ‾‾ ‾‾ ‾‾ ‾‾ ‾‾ ‾‾ ‾‾ ‾‾ ‾‾ ‾‾ ‾‾ ‾‾ ‾‾
14 12 3   7   4 14 12 3 6 9 8 6 8 3 7 4

      U
‾‾ ‾‾ ‾‾ ‾‾ ‾‾ ‾‾ ‾‾ ‾‾ ‾‾ ‾‾ ‾‾ ‾‾ ‾‾ ‾‾ ‾‾ ‾‾ ‾‾
11 12 10 5   1 12 5 4 2 13 8 9 6 4 10 9 4

1-10 TI-73 Activity

Function Tables

Create function tables with a TI-73 graphing calculator by using the LIST feature.

Example   Create a function table for the function rule $3n + 2$.
Use input values $-4, 2, 0,$ and 5.

Step 1   Clear all lists.
[2nd] [MEM] 6 [ENTER]

Step 2   Create a new list in a blank-list position. [LIST]

Step 3   Label the list *INPUT*.
[2nd] [TEXT] I N P U T Done [ENTER] [ENTER]

Step 4   Enter the input values: $-4, 2, 0,$ and 5.
Press **ENTER** after each value.

Step 5   Create another list in a different blank-list position.
Label it *OUTPUT*. (See step 3.)

Step 6   Enter the function rule, $3n + 2$, in the *OUTPUT* list.
[2nd] [TEXT] " Done

3 [×] [2nd] [STAT] (choose the list *INPUT*)

[+] 2 [2nd] [TEXT] " Done [ENTER] [ENTER]

```
L6      INPUT  OUTPU▸ B
------   -4     -10
          2      8
          0      2
          5     17
------   ------  ------
OUTPU(1)= -10
```

Step 7   Observe the values in the *OUTPUT* list. Choose 3 more input values.
Enter them in the *INPUT* list. Observe the corresponding output values.

Exercises

Complete each function table.

1.

Input (n)	Output ($-4n$)
−3	
−1	
0	
1	
3	

2.

Input (n)	Output $\left(\dfrac{-n}{2}\right)$
−24	
−10	
15	
30	
45	

3.

Input (n)	Output ($-2n - 6$)
12	
8	
3	
−7	
−15	

4.

Input (n)	Output ($-3n + 1$)	Output ($6n - 8$)
15		
10		
6		
−25		
−32		

Lesson 1-10

1 Student Recording Sheet

Use this recording sheet with pages 76–77 of the Student Edition.

Part 1: Multiple Choice

Read each question. Then fill in the correct answer.

1. Ⓐ Ⓑ Ⓒ Ⓓ

2. Ⓕ Ⓖ Ⓗ Ⓙ

3. Ⓐ Ⓑ Ⓒ Ⓓ

4. Ⓕ Ⓖ Ⓗ Ⓙ

5. Ⓐ Ⓑ Ⓒ Ⓓ

6. Ⓕ Ⓖ Ⓗ Ⓙ

7. Ⓐ Ⓑ Ⓒ Ⓓ

8. Ⓕ Ⓖ Ⓗ Ⓙ

Part 2: Short Response/Grid in

Record your answer in the blank.

9. _____

10. _____

11. _____

12. _____

Part 3: Extended Response

Record your answers for Question 13 on the back of this paper.

Assessment

1 Rubric for Scoring Extended Response

(Use to score the Extended-Response question on page 77 of the Student Edition.)

General Scoring Guidelines

- If a student gives only a correct numerical answer to a problem but does not show how he or she arrived at the answer, the student will be awarded only 1 credit. All extended response questions require the student to show work.

- A fully correct answer for a multiple-part question requires correct responses for all parts of the question. For example, if a question has three parts, the correct response to one or two parts of the question that required work to be shown is *not* considered a fully correct response.

- Students who use trial and error to solve a problem must show their method. Merely showing that the answer checks or is correct is not considered a complete response for full credit.

Exercise 13 Rubric

Score	Specific Criteria
4	The third term is correctly drawn. The rule $6x - 2$ is correctly identified.
3	The third term is correctly drawn, but the rule is incorrectly stated **OR** The third term is incorrectly drawn, but the rule is correctly stated.
2	The third term is correctly drawn, but the rule is not stated. **OR** The third term is not drawn, but the rule is correctly stated.
1	The third term is not drawn and the rule is incorrectly stated. **OR** The third term is incorrectly drawn and the rule is not stated.
0	Response is completely incorrect.

NAME _____ DATE _____ PERIOD _____

Chapter 1 Quiz 1

(Lessons 1-1 through 1-3)

SCORE _____

BICYCLES For Exercises 1 and 2, use the following information. Alonso wants to buy a bicycle that costs $180. So far, he has saved $95. If he wants to buy the bicycle in 5 weeks, how much should he save each week?

1. State the operations or problem-solving strategies that you would use to solve the problem.

1. _____

2. Use the four-step plan to solve the problem.

2. _____

Evaluate each expression.

3. 3^4 **4.** 8^2 **5.** 10^5

3. _____

4. _____

5. _____

6. What is 5^3 written as a product of the same factor?

6. _____

Find the square of each number.

7. 23   **8.** 43   **9.** 36

7. _____

8. _____

9. _____

10. Find the square root of 361.

10. _____

NAME _____ DATE _____ PERIOD _____

Chapter 1 Quiz 2

(Lessons 1-4 and 1-5)

SCORE _____

Evaluate each expression.

1. $(2 + 9) \cdot (13 - 8)$

1. _____

2. $36 \div 9 \times 4 - 1$

2. _____

3. $(5 + 2)^2 + 3$

3. _____

4. Malcolm is buying three tacos and an iced tea. What expression represents the total cost?

Item	Cost ($)
taco	0.79
iced tea	1.05

4. _____

5. A number is subtracted from 8. Then 12 is divided by the result. The final answer is 3. What is the number?

5. _____

Assessment

1) Chapter 1 Quiz 3

(Lessons 1-6 through 1-8)

Evaluate each expression if $d = 6$, $e = 2$, $f = 3$, and $g = 5$.

1. $f + 7$

1. _____

2. $2g - 3e$

2. _____

3. $\dfrac{6d}{e^2}$

3. _____

4. What value of x is a solution of $x + 13 = 29$?

4. _____

5. Name the property shown by the following statement.
   $3 + (7 + 5) = (3 + 7) + 5$

5. _____

- -

1) Chapter 1 Quiz 4

(Lessons 1-9 and 1-10)

Describe the relationship between the terms in each arithmetic sequence. Then write the next three terms in each sequence.

1. 1, 6, 11, 16, …

1. _____

2. 29, 33, 37, 41, …

2. _____

3. **MULTIPLE CHOICE** The table shows the number of car wash flyers that Jeanette distributes in a given number of days. Which function rule represents the data?

Number of Days (x)	Total Number of Flyers (y)
1	15
2	30
3	45

   A. $y = 3x$ **B.** $y = 5x$ **C.** $y = 15x$ **D.** $y = 30x$

3. _____

For Exercises 4 and 5, use the following statement.
One number is 7 less than the second number.

4. Write an equation using two variables to show the relationship between the first number f and the second number s.

4. _____

5. What is the second number if the first number is 18?

5. _____

1 **Chapter 1 Mid-Chapter Test**

(Lessons 1-1 through 1-6)

PART I

Write the letter for the correct answer in the blank at the right of each question.

1. Which of the following is not a step in the four-step plan for solving problems?

   A. solve   **B.** plan   **C.** match   **D.** explore   1. _____

Evaluate each expression.

2. $21 + 15 \div 3$

   F. 26   **G.** 12   **H.** 25   **J.** 39   2. _____

3. $\dfrac{(r + 2)^2}{s}$ if $r = 3$ and $s = 5$

   A. $\dfrac{7}{5}$ **B.** 5   **C.** 1   **D.** $\dfrac{49}{3}$ 3. _____

4. Find 9^2.

   F. 3   **G.** 11   **H.** 18   **J.** 81   4. _____

5. Find $\sqrt{144}$.

   A. 12   **B.** 13   **C.** 72   **D.** 20,736   5. _____

PART II

6. Find the square of 16.   6. _____

7. Identify the coefficient, variable, and constant in the expression $3s - 7$.   7. _____

8. **THEATER** A theater holds 1,450 people. If 950 people can be seated on the main floor, how many seats are available in the balcony?   8. _____

Write each product in exponential form.

9. $3 \cdot 3 \cdot 3 \cdot 3 \cdot 3$ 10. $10 \cdot 10 \cdot 10 \cdot 10$ 9. _____

    10. _____

Evaluate.

11. 2^8 12. 7^3 11. _____

    12. _____

13. **FIELD TRIPS** To attend a class field trip, each student had to pay $5 for the theater ticket and $2.50 for transportation. A total of $1,275 was collected. How many students went on the field trip?   13. _____

Assessment

1 Chapter 1 Vocabulary Test/Review

SCORE _____

algebra	evaluate	radical sign
algebraic expression	exponent	range
arithmetic sequence	factors	sequence
base	function	solution
coefficient	function rule	square
defining the variable	numerical expression	square root
domain	order of operations	term
equation	perfect square	variable
equivalent expressions	powers	

Choose from the terms above to complete each sentence.

1. The numbers 2, 5, 8, 11, … are an example of a(n) _____.   1. _____

2. To _____ a number means to multiply that number by itself. 2. _____

3. A(n) _____ is the symbol used to indicate the positive square root of a number.   3. _____

4. A(n) _____ contains variables, numbers, and at least one operation.   4. _____

5. The numerical factor of a term that contains a variable is called a(n) _____.   5. _____

6. A(n) _____ tells how many times a base is used as a factor.   6. _____

7. Mathematicians agreed on a(n) _____ so that numerical expressions would have only one value.   7. _____

8. A(n) _____ is a mathematical sentence that contains an equals sign.   8. _____

9. A relationship in which each input value results in exactly one output value is called a(n) _____.   9. _____

10. The _____ of a function is the set of output values.   10. _____

Define each term in your own words.

11. solution   11. _____

12. variable   12. _____

1 Chapter 1 Test, Form 1

Write the letter for the correct answer in the blank at the right of each question.

1. **SNACKS** Charlie is responsible for bringing snacks to the soccer game. He has $20, and there are 10 players on the team. How much can he spend on each snack?

   A. $1   **B.** $2   **C.** $10   **D.** $20   1. _____

2. Write 1^4 as a product of the same factor.

   F. $1 \cdot 1 \cdot 1 \cdot 1$ **G.** $1 \cdot 4$ **H.** 4   **J.** $4 \cdot 4 \cdot 4 \cdot 4$ 2. _____

3. Evaluate 3^3.

   A. 81   **B.** 27   **C.** $3 \cdot 3 \cdot 3$ **D.** 9   3. _____

4. Write $5 \cdot 5$ in exponential form.

   F. 25   **G.** 5^5 **H.** 5^2 **J.** $5 \cdot 2$ 4. _____

5. Find $\sqrt{2,500}$.

   A. 50   **B.** 25   **C.** 10   **D.** 7   5. _____

6. Find 18^2.

   F. 18   **G.** 36   **H.** 162   **J.** 324   6. _____

Evaluate each expression.

7. $(3 + 4) \times 5$

   A. 7   **B.** 23   **C.** 30   **D.** 35   7. _____

8. $5 \cdot 2 + 8$

   F. 50   **G.** 18   **H.** 15   **J.** 10   8. _____

9. $9 - 3 + 4$

   A. 10   **B.** 8   **C.** 6   **D.** 2   9. _____

10. **MONEY** Ron has $1.35 in dimes and quarters in his pocket. If there are twice as many dimes in his pocket as quarters, how many quarters does he have?

    F. 1   **G.** 3   **H.** 4   **J.** 6   10. _____

11. **NUMBERS** A number is squared and then 5 is subtracted from the result. The final answer is 44. What is the number?

    A. 5   **B.** 6   **C.** 7   **D.** 8   11. _____

Evaluate each expression.

12. $f + 8$ if $f = 7$

    F. 8   **G.** 15   **H.** 56   **J.** 78   12. _____

13. $6x$ if $x = 5$

    A. 11   **B.** 30   **C.** 6^5 **D.** 65   13. _____

Assessment

Chapter 1 Test, Form 1 *(continued)*

14. Evaluate $r - s$ if $r = 15$ and $s = 10$.

    F. 25   **G.** 10   **H.** 15   **J.** 5   **14.** _____

For Questions 15–17, solve each equation mentally.

15. $3 + x = 10$

    A. 6   **B.** 7   **C.** 8   **D.** 13   **15.** _____

16. $24 - 17 = n$

    F. 41   **G.** 8   **H.** 7   **J.** 6   **16.** _____

17. $\dfrac{t}{5} = 9$

    A. 1.8   **B.** 5   **C.** 9   **D.** 45   **17.** _____

18. Name the property of multiplication shown by $6 \cdot 4 = 4 \cdot 6$.

    F. Associative   **G.** Commutative   **H.** Distributive   **J.** Identity   **18.** _____

19. Use the Distributive Property to write $2(5 + 3)$ as an equivalent expression. Then evaluate the expression.

    A. 2(8); 16   **B.** 2(5) + 2(3); 16   **C.** 2(5) + 3; 13   **D.** (5 + 3)2; 16   **19.** _____

20. Name the property of addition shown by $3 + 0 = 3$.

    F. Associative   **G.** Commutative   **H.** Distributive   **J.** Identity   **20.** _____

Identify the next three terms in each sequence.

21. 4, 8, 12, 16, ...

    A. 18, 20, 21   **B.** 18, 22, 26   **C.** 20, 24, 28   **D.** 32, 48, 64   **21.** _____

22. 1, 7, 13, 19, ...

    F. 133, 931, 6517   **G.** 26, 33, 40   **H.** 25, 31, 37   **J.** 19, 25, 31   **22.** _____

23. 11, 16, 21, 26, ...

    A. 31, 36, 41   **B.** 31, 35, 39   **C.** 30, 34, 38   **D.** 30, 36, 41   **23.** _____

JOBS For Questions 24 and 25, use the following information.
Jessica charges $8 per hour for mowing lawns.

24. Write an equation to show the relationship between the total cost c of mowing a lawn in h hours.

    F. $c = h + 8$ **G.** $h = c + 8$ **H.** $c = 8h$ **J.** $h = 8c$ **24.** _____

25. How much will it cost to have Jessica mow a lawn if it takes her 3 hours?

    A. $5   **B.** $9   **C.** $11   **D.** $24   **25.** _____

Bonus What value of x makes the expressions $x + 2$ and $2x$ equal? **B:** _____

1 **Chapter 1 Test, Form 2A** SCORE _____

Write the letter for the correct answer in the blank at the right of each question.

1. **COMPUTERS** Lance wants to buy a computer that costs $1,250 with tax. So far, he has saved $750. If he saves $125 every week, in how many weeks will he be able to purchase the computer?

   A. 3 weeks   **B.** 4 weeks   **C.** 6 weeks   **D.** 10 weeks   1. _____

2. Write 5^4 as a product of the same factor.

   F. 625   **G.** $4 \cdot 4 \cdot 4 \cdot 4 \cdot 4$ **H.** $5 \cdot 5 \cdot 5 \cdot 5$ **J.** $5 \cdot 4$ 2. _____

3. Evaluate 2^6.

   A. 64   **B.** 36   **C.** 12   **D.** 26   3. _____

4. Write $11 \cdot 11 \cdot 11 \cdot 11$ in exponential form.

   F. 4^{11} **G.** 11^4 **H.** 44   **J.** 16,641   4. _____

5. Find the square of 30.

   A. 3   **B.** 90   **C.** 300   **D.** 900   5. _____

6. Find $\sqrt{529}$.

   F. 22   **G.** 23   **H.** 25   **J.** 29   6. _____

7. Evaluate $15 + 6 \div 3$.

   A. 24   **B.** 18   **C.** 17   **D.** 7   7. _____

8. Evaluate $4 + 8 \div 4 - 2$.

   F. 0   **G.** 1   **H.** 4   **J.** 6   8. _____

9. Evaluate $9 + 2(5 - 3) - 6$.

   A. 1   **B.** 7   **C.** 9   **D.** 13   9. _____

10. **MONEY** Carina has twice as many quarters as dimes. If she has $3.60, how many quarters does she have?

    F. 3   **G.** 6   **H.** 12   **J.** 18   10. _____

11. **ENTERTAINMENT** Gabriel used a total of 17 tokens playing video games. Some games required 2 tokens and others required 3 tokens. How many 2-token games could he have played?

    A. 2   **B.** 3   **C.** 4   **D.** 5   11. _____

12. Evaluate $\dfrac{3r}{s^2}$ if $r = 8$ and $s = 2$.

    F. 4   **G.** 6   **H.** 12   **J.** 24   12. _____

13. Evaluate $3a + 4b$ if $a = 3$ and $b = 7$.

    A. 7   **B.** 12   **C.** 33   **D.** 37   13. _____

Assessment

1 **Chapter 1 Test, Form 2A** (continued)

14. Evaluate $6f^2 + 10$ if $f = 3$.

    F. 64   **G.** 54   **H.** 44   **J.** 19   **14.** _____

For Questions 15–17, solve each equation mentally.

15. $a - 19 = 20$

    A. 1   **B.** 29   **C.** 39   **D.** 380   **15.** _____

16. $2d = 66$

    F. 30   **G.** 33   **H.** 64   **J.** 132   **16.** _____

17. $42 = y + 31$

    A. 9   **B.** 11   **C.** 19   **D.** 21   **17.** _____

18. Use the Distributive Property to write $3(9 + 2)$ as an equivalent expression. Then evaluate the expression.

    F. 3(11); 33   **G.** (9 + 2); 30   **H.** 3(9) + 3(2); 30   **J.** 3(9) + 3(2); 33 **18.** _____

Name the property of multiplication shown by each statement.

19. $13 \times 12 = 12 \times 13$

    A. Associative   **B.** Commutative   **C.** Distributive   **D.** Identity   **19.** _____

20. $(3 \times 6) \times 4 = 3 \times (6 \times 4)$

    F. Associative   **G.** Commutative   **H.** Distributive   **J.** Identity   **20.** _____

Identify the next three terms in each sequence.

21. 3, 6, 9, 12, …

    A. 24, 48, 96   **B.** 14, 16, 18   **C.** 15, 18, 21   **D.** 15, 17, 20   **21.** _____

22. 15, 26, 37, 48, …

    F. 57, 66, 75   **G.** 58, 68, 78   **H.** 58, 69, 80   **J.** 59, 70, 81   **22.** _____

23. 2.0, 3.5, 5.0, 6.5, …

    A. 8.5, 9.0, 11.5   **C.** 8.0, 9.5, 11

    B. 8.25, 53.625, 348.5625   **D.** 7.0, 8.5, 9.0   **23.** _____

JOBS Charles charges $6 an hour to babysit.

24. Write an equation to show the relationship between the total cost c that Charles will charge for babysitting for h hours.

    F. $c = h + 6$ **G.** $h = c + 6$ **H.** $c = 6h$ **J.** $h = 6c$ **24.** _____

25. How much will Charles charge to baby-sit for 4 hours?

    A. $1.50   **B.** $10.00   **C.** $16.00   **D.** $24.00   **25.** _____

Bonus GROCERIES Bethany purchased 3 cans of soup for $0.79 each and 4 boxes of crackers for $1.39 each. Write and then evaluate an expression for the total cost of the groceries.   **B:** _____

1 | Chapter 1 Test, Form 2B

SCORE _____

Write the letter for the correct answer in the blank at the right of each question.

1. **MONEY** Ching-Li wants to buy a lawn mower that costs \$1,925 with tax. So far, he has saved \$650. If he saves \$425 each month, in how many months will he be able to purchase the lawn mower?

   A. 3 months   **B.** 4 months   **C.** 5 months   **D.** 9 months   1. _____

2. Write 7^3 as a product of the same factor.

   F. $3 \cdot 3 \cdot 3 \cdot 3 \cdot 3 \cdot 3 \cdot 3$ **H.** $7 \cdot 3$

   G. $7 \cdot 7 \cdot 7$ **J.** 343 2. _____

3. Evaluate 4^3.

   A. 12   **B.** 81   **C.** $4 \cdot 4 \cdot 4$ **D.** 64   3. _____

4. Write $10 \cdot 10 \cdot 10 \cdot 10 \cdot 10$ in exponential form.

   F. 10^5 **G.** 5^{10} **H.** 100,000   **J.** 50   4. _____

5. Find the square of 20.

   A. 2   **B.** 40   **C.** 200   **D.** 400   5. _____

6. Find $\sqrt{676}$.

   F. 22   **G.** 25   **H.** 26   **J.** 28   6. _____

Evaluate each expression.

7. $20 + 12 \div 4$

   A. 3   **B.** 8   **C.** 23   **D.** 32   7. _____

8. $6 + 10 \div 2 - 5$

   F. 0   **G.** 3   **H.** 6   **J.** 13   8. _____

9. $11 + 4(7 - 3) - 7$

   A. 60.5   **B.** 36   **C.** 20   **D.** 18   9. _____

10. **MONEY** Josh has twice as many dimes as nickels. If he has \$1.75, how many nickels does he have?

    F. 6   **G.** 7   **H.** 14   **J.** 15   10. _____

11. **ENTERTAINMENT** Emilia bought a total of 14 designer pens for her friends. The pens came in 2-packs and 3-packs. How many 3-packs did she buy?

    A. 2   **B.** 3   **C.** 5   **D.** 6   11. _____

12. Evaluate $\dfrac{9r}{s^2}$ if $r = 6$ and $s = 3$.

    F. 27   **G.** 9   **H.** 6   **J.** 4.5   12. _____

13. Evaluate $5a + 7b$ if $a = 4$ and $b = 3$.

    A. 41   **B.** 12   **C.** 43   **D.** 35   13. _____

Assessment

1 **Chapter 1 Test, Form 2B** *(continued)*

14. Evaluate $12f^2 + 9$ if $f = 2$.

    F. 33   **G.** 39   **H.** 48   **J.** 57   14. _____

For Questions 15–17, solve each equation mentally.

15. $a - 15 = 30$

    A. 15   **B.** 45   **C.** 55   **D.** 450   15. _____

16. $2d = 44$

    F. 20   **G.** 22   **H.** 42   **J.** 88   16. _____

17. $36 = x + 24$

    A. 11   **B.** 12   **C.** 21   **D.** 22   17. _____

18. Use the Distributive Property to write $2(3 + 9)$ as an equivalent expression. Then evaluate the expression.

    F. $2(12)$; 24   **G.** $2(3) + 2(9)$; 23   **H.** $2(3) + 2(9)$; 24   **J.** $(3 + 9)2$; 23   18. _____

Name the property of addition shown by each statement.

19. $3 + 7 = 7 + 3$

    A. Associative   **B.** Commutative   **C.** Distributive   **D.** Identity   19. _____

20. $4 + (9 + 12) = (4 + 9) + 12$

    F. Associative   **G.** Commutative   **H.** Distributive   **J.** Identity   20. _____

Identify the next three terms in each sequence.

21. 9, 13, 17, 21, …

    A. 24, 27, 31   **B.** 21, 25, 29   **C.** 24, 29, 33   **D.** 25, 29, 33   21. _____

22. 17, 28, 39, 50, …

    F. 61, 71, 81   **G.** 61, 72, 83   **H.** 60, 71, 82   **J.** 59, 68, 77   22. _____

23. 3.2, 4.4, 5.6, 6.8, …

    A. 6.8, 8.0, 9.2   **C.** 8.0, 9.2, 10.4

    B. 8.0, 9.2, 10.6   **D.** 9.35, 63.58, 432.344   23. _____

PHONES A phone service charges its customers $24 per month.

24. Write an equation to show the relationship between the total cost c for m months.

    F. $c = 24m$ **G.** $m = 24c$ **H.** $c = m + 24$ **J.** $m = c + 24$ 24. _____

25. How much will the service cost for 6 months?

    A. $144   **B.** $30   **C.** $12   **D.** $4   25. _____

Bonus GROCERIES Kirima purchased 4 fruit bars for $0.75 each and 3 bags of trail mix for $1.59 each. Write and then evaluate an expression for the total cost of the snacks.   **B:** _____

1 Chapter 1 Test, Form 2C

SCORE ____

1. **TICKET SALES** A movie theater took in $17,500 in ticket sales during the first week of December. The attendance in the first week of January is expected to be triple that amount. Use the four-step plan to find the expected number of people that will attend during the first week in January if tickets cost $5 each.

1. _____

2. Write 4^5 as a product of the same factor.

2. _____

3. Evaluate 2^7.

3. _____

4. Write $3 \cdot 3 \cdot 3 \cdot 3 \cdot 3$ in exponential form.

4. _____

Find the square of each number.

5. 9

5. _____

6. 40

6. _____

Find each square root.

7. $\sqrt{144}$

7. _____

8. $\sqrt{1,369}$

8. _____

Evaluate each expression.

9. $10 + 8 \div 2$

9. _____

10. $32 \div 4(8)$

10. _____

11. $3 \times 7 - 2^2$

11. _____

12. $4 + (9 - 6 + 5)^2$

12. _____

13. **MONEY** Kia has 8 coins that total $1.15. How many quarters, dimes, and nickels does she have?

13. _____

Evaluate each expression if $a = 2$, $b = 6$, $c = 3$, and $d = 5$.

14. $8c$

14. _____

15. $11 - 3a$

15. _____

16. $7b - 5d$

16. _____

17. $\dfrac{10b}{a^2}$

17. _____

Name the number that is the solution of the given equation.

18. $8 + r = 23$; 13, 14, 15

18. _____

19. $n \div 10 = 5$; 5, 50, 500

19. _____

87

Assessment

1   Chapter 1 Test, Form 2C   (continued)

Solve each equation mentally.

20. $a - 12 = 30$

20. _____

21. $9 = \dfrac{y}{3}$

21. _____

22. SWIMMING Rita swam 3 more laps than Lin in the last
swimming team practice. Lin swam 14 laps, and Rita swam
r laps. Write an equation and solve.

22. _____

23. MONEY Conner buys a muffin and a bottle of orange juice
for breakfast for a total of $2.75. The orange juice cost $1.55.
Write and solve an equation to find the cost of the
muffin m.

23. _____

Use the Distributive Property to evaluate each expression.

24. $(9 + 2)7$

24. _____

25. $3(12 - 5)$

25. _____

Name the property shown by each statement.

26. $(8 \times 2) \times 5 = 8 \times (2 \times 5)$

26. _____

27. $13 + 0 = 13$

27. _____

**Describe the relationship between the terms in each
arithmetic sequence.**

28. 1, 3.5, 6, 8.5, …

28. _____

29. 18, 25, 32, 39, …

29. _____

Write the next three terms of each sequence.

30. 3.4, 6.4, 9.4, 12.4, …

30. _____

31. 6, 12, 18, 24, …

31. _____

**JOBS For Questions 32 and 33, use the following information.
Jake earns $7 per hour working at a dog kennel.**

32. Write an equation to show the relationship between his total
earnings y for x hours worked.

32. _____

33. How much does Jake earn in a two-week period if he worked
a total of 15 hours?

33. _____

1 **Chapter 1 Test, Form 2D**   SCORE _____

1. **SALES** A plant nursery took in $2,400 in sales of 4-inch potted annuals during March. April sales are expected to be triple that amount. Use the four-step plan to find the expected number of 4-inch potted annuals sold in April if each costs $2.   1. _____

2. Write 3^6 as a product of the same factor.   2. _____

3. Evaluate 5^3.   3. _____

4. Write $7 \cdot 7 \cdot 7 \cdot 7 \cdot 7$ in exponential form.   4. _____

Find the square of each number.

5. 4   5. _____

6. 30   6. _____

Find the square root.

7. $\sqrt{121}$ 7. _____

8. $\sqrt{1,089}$ 8. _____

Evaluate each expression.

9. $12 + 9 \div 3$ 9. _____

10. $18 \div 3(2)$ 10. _____

11. $7 \times 4 - 3^2$ 11. _____

12. $5 + (7 - 4 + 2)^2$ 12. _____

13. **MONEY** Lara has 8 coins that total $1.35. How many quarters, dimes, and nickels does she have?   13. _____

Evaluate each expression if $a = 3$, $b = 7$, $c = 2$, and $d = 8$.

14. $7b$ 14. _____

15. $12 - 4c$ 15. _____

16. $8a - 2d$ 16. _____

17. $\dfrac{6d}{c^2}$ 17. _____

Name the number that is the solution of the given equation.

18. $7 + r = 25$; 18, 19, 20   18. _____

19. $n \div 10 = 8$; 8, 80, 800   19. _____

Assessment

1 **Chapter 1 Test, Form 2D** *(continued)*

Solve each equation mentally.

20. $a - 17 = 22$

20. _____

21. $12 = \dfrac{y}{4}$

21. _____

22. TRACK LeRoy ran 4 more laps than Ben in the last track team practice. Ben ran 6 laps, and LeRoy ran r laps. Write an equation and solve.

22. _____

23. MONEY Emily buys a bagel and a cup of hot chocolate for breakfast for a total of $2.85. The bagel cost $1.15. Write and solve an equation that could be used to find the cost of the hot chocolate h.

23. _____

Use the Distributive Property to evaluate each expression.

24. $(7 + 3)5$

24. _____

25. $4(10 - 7)$

25. _____

Name the property shown by each statement.

26. $8 + 12 = 12 + 8$

26. _____

27. $18 \times 1 = 18$

27. _____

Describe the relationship between the terms in each arithmetic sequence.

28. $2, 4.1, 6.2, 8.3, \ldots$

28. _____

29. $17, 22, 27, 32, \ldots$

29. _____

Write the next three terms of each sequence.

30. $5.3, 10.3, 15.3, 20.3, \ldots$

30. _____

31. $4, 12, 20, 28, \ldots$

31. _____

PHONES For Questions 32 and 33, use the following information.
Carmen earns $8 per hour working part-time at an animal hospital.

32. Write an equation to show the relationship between her total earnings y for x hours worked.

32. _____

33. How much will Carmen earn in a month if she works a total of 22 hours?

33. _____

Bonus Insert operation symbols to make the equation true.

$8 \,\square\, 2 \,\square\, 10 \,\square\, 2 = 11$

B: _____

1 Chapter 1 Test, Form 3

For Questions 1 and 2, use the four-step plan to solve each problem.

1. **AVIATION** If an airplane departs from an airport every 5 minutes, how many airplane departures are expected from 9:30 A.M. to 11:00 A.M.?

1. _____

2. **GARDENS** Pam's garden covers a 1,200-square-foot area. She maintains 6,000 plants. What is the number of plants per square foot?

2. _____

3. Evaluate 13 to the second power.

3. _____

4. Express 729 in exponential form as a power of 3.

4. _____

5. Use exponents to write $7 \cdot 7 \cdot 7 \cdot 2 \cdot 2 \cdot 2 \cdot 2$ in the shortest form possible.

5. _____

Find the square of each number.

6. 19

6. _____

7. 32

7. _____

Find the square root.

8. $\sqrt{441}$

8. _____

9. $\sqrt{256}$

9. _____

Evaluate each expression.

10. $24 \div 2 - 4(7 - 5) + 8$

10. _____

11. $(8 + 1)^2 - 3(2)$

11. _____

12. Insert parentheses to make $40 \div 2 + 8 - 2 = 2$ true.

12. _____

13. **FUNDRAISING** Volleyball team players are raising money by selling school mascot bracelets for $2 and buttons for $1. They hope to earn $165 and plan to sell 100 items in all. How many do they need to sell?

13. _____

14. Summarize the difference between an expression and an equation. Then give an example of each.

14. _____

15. Evaluate $4x + x^2 - x$ if $x = 5$.

15. _____

Assessment

1 **Chapter 1 Test, Form 3** (continued)

16. **MEASUREMENT** Complete the table and write an equation to describe the pattern.

Feet (*f*)	Yards (*y*)
1	$\frac{1}{3}$
2	$\frac{2}{3}$
3	?
8	?
12	?

16. _____

Solve each equation mentally.

17. $16j = 320$

17. _____

18. $n - 27 = 135$

18. _____

19. Consider the equation $a \div 1 = b$. What can you say about *a* and *b*?

19. _____

Use properties to simplify each expression.

20. $(14 + 8b) + 3$

20. _____

21. $9(z + 7)$

21. _____

Describe the relationship between the terms in each arithmetic sequence. Then write the next three terms.

22. 17, 22, 27, 32, ...

22. _____

23. 4.5, 13.5, 22.5, 31.5, ...

23. _____

24. 5.0, 6.3, 7.6, 8.9, ...

24. _____

25. **ANTELOPES** American antelopes can run long distances at 35 miles per hour. Write an equation to show the number of miles *m* an antelope can run in *h* hours. Then find the number of miles it can travel at that rate in 3.5 hours.

25. _____

Bonus Use properties to simplify the expression
$18 + 2(3 + a) - 5 \cdot 2$

B: _____

1 Chapter 1 Extended-Response Test

Demonstrate your knowledge by giving a clear, concise solution to each problem. Be sure to include all relevant drawings and justify your answers. You may show your solution in more than one way or investigate beyond the requirements of the problem. If necessary, record your answer on another piece of paper.

1. Evaluate $7p + 6(p \div q)^2 - 2q$ if $p = 6$ and $q = 3$. Show your work and give an explanation for each step.

2. **MOVIE TICKETS** For a class trip, a teacher bought 25 student tickets and 5 adult tickets.

   a. Write an equation for the total number of tickets purchased. Solve this equation.

   b. If student tickets cost $4 each and adult tickets cost $6 each, how much money did the teacher spend on tickets? Use the four-step plan.

3. Describe the pattern in the following sequence and explain how you would find the next term in the sequence.
   752, 756, 760, 764, 768, …

4. Explain in your own words what is meant by the *square root* of a number.

Assessment

1 Standardized Test Practice

SCORE _____

(Chapter 1)

Part 1: Multiple Choice

Instructions: Fill in the appropriate circle for the best answer.

1. **SALES** In one week, a computer retailer took in $1,863,520 in orders for new computers. When a promotion is announced for the following week, the company expects to receive twice as many orders. Find the expected sales during the week of the promotion. (Lesson 1-1)

   A $931,760   **C** $2,862,520

   B $1,862,520   **D** $3,727,040   1. Ⓐ Ⓑ Ⓒ Ⓓ

2. Evaluate 2^4. (Lesson 1-2)

   F $2 \cdot 2 \cdot 2 \cdot 2 \cdot 2$ **H** 16

   G 8   **J** 32   2. Ⓕ Ⓖ Ⓗ Ⓙ

3. Write the product $8 \cdot 8 \cdot 8$ in exponential form. (Lesson 1-2)

   A $8 \cdot 3$ **B** 3^8 **C** 8^3 **D** 512   3. Ⓐ Ⓑ Ⓒ Ⓓ

4. Find $\sqrt{361}$. (Lesson 1-3)

   F 16   **G** 17   **H** 18   **J** 19   4. Ⓕ Ⓖ Ⓗ Ⓙ

5. **ROOMS** A square room has an area of 169 square feet. What is the perimeter of the room? (Lesson 1-3)

   A 13 ft   **B** 17 ft   **C** 52 ft   **D** 676 ft   5. Ⓐ Ⓑ Ⓒ Ⓓ

6. Evaluate $36 \div 6 + 12 \div 2$. (Lesson 1-4)

   F 12   **G** 3   **H** 1   **J** 0   6. Ⓕ Ⓖ Ⓗ Ⓙ

7. **MONEY** Jackie is buying 3 gallons of lemonade and 2 gallons of orange juice. What is the total cost? (Lesson 1-4)

   A $12   **B** $16

   C $14   **D** $18

Beverage	Price per Gallon
lemonade	$2
orange juice	$4

   7. Ⓐ Ⓑ Ⓒ Ⓓ

8. **GEOMETRY** The perimeter of a rectangle is 46 centimeters and its area is 126 square centimeters. What are the dimensions of the rectangle? (Lesson 1-5)

   F 6 cm by 21 cm   **H** 9 cm by 14 cm

   G 8 cm by 12 cm   **I** 10 cm by 13 cm   8. Ⓕ Ⓖ Ⓗ Ⓙ

9. Evaluate $11x - y$ if $x = 2$ and $y = 4$. (Lesson 1-6)

   A 8   **B** 18   **C** 11   **D** 42   9. Ⓐ Ⓑ Ⓒ Ⓓ

1 Standardized Test Practice (continued)
(*Chapter 1*)

10. Evaluate $\dfrac{4d^2}{e}$ if $d = 3$ and $e = 2$. (Lesson 1-6)

    F $\dfrac{16}{3}$ **G** 6   **H** 12   **J** 18   10. Ⓕ Ⓖ Ⓗ Ⓙ

11. Solve $18 - n = 10$. (Lesson 1-7)

    A 8   **B** 18   **C** 28   **D** 38   11. Ⓐ Ⓑ Ⓒ Ⓓ

12. Solve $\dfrac{z}{6} = 11$. (Lesson 1-7)

    F $\dfrac{6}{11}$ **G** $\dfrac{11}{6}$ **H** 5   **J** 66   12. Ⓕ Ⓖ Ⓗ Ⓙ

13. Name the property shown by the statement $(5 + 8)r = 5r + 8r$. (Lesson 1-8)

    A Associative Property of Addition
    B Associative Property of Multiplication
    C Commutative Property of Multiplication
    D Distributive Property   13. Ⓐ Ⓑ Ⓒ Ⓓ

14. Name the property of multiplication shown by the statement $(a \times b) \times c = a \times (b \times c)$. (Lesson 1-8)

    F Associative
    G Commutative
    H Distributive
    J Identity   14. Ⓕ Ⓖ Ⓗ Ⓙ

15. Write the next three terms of the sequence 9, 17, 25, 33, …
    (Lesson 1-9)

    A 41, 49, 57   **C** 38, 43, 48
    B 40, 47, 54   **D** 36, 39, 42   15. Ⓐ Ⓑ Ⓒ Ⓓ

16. **COLLECTIONS** Ron is starting a coin collection. Each month, he buys 3 coins. Suppose he continues this pattern. What algebraic expression can be used to find the number of coins in his collection after any number of months n? (Lesson 1-9)

    F n^3 **H** $n + 3$
    G $3n$ **J** $n - 3$ 16. Ⓕ Ⓖ Ⓗ Ⓙ

17. Evaluate 10^2. (Lesson 1-2)

    A 10   **B** 20   **C** 100   **D** 200   17. Ⓐ Ⓑ Ⓒ Ⓓ

18. Solve $11 \cdot 3 = m$. (Lesson 1-7)

    F 8   **G** 14   **H** 33   **J** 113   18. Ⓕ Ⓖ Ⓗ Ⓙ

Assessment

1 Standardized Test Practice (continued)

(Chapter 1)

Part 2: Short Response

Instructions: Write answers to short response in the space provided.

19. **DRAGONFLIES** A dragonfly can fly at 36 miles per hour. At this rate, about how far can it fly in 10 minutes? (Lesson 1-1)

19. _____

20. Evaluate $12 - (5 + 4)$. (Lesson 1-4)

20. _____

21. **NUMBERS** Sixteen is added to a number. Then 5 is multiplied by the sum. The result is 125. What is the number? (Lesson 1-5)

21. _____

22. Solve $g + 34 = 64$. (Lesson 1-7)

22. _____

23. Name the property of multiplication shown by the statement $12 \times 8 = 8 \times 12$. (Lesson 1-8)

23. _____

24. **RIDES** The table shows the number of times an amusement park ride spins for a given number of minutes. If the ride lasts 5 minutes, how many revolutions would there be? (Lesson 1-10)

Number of Minutes	Number of Revolutions
1	12
2	24
3	36
4	48

24. _____

25. **COOKING** Grace is serving pork roast for a holiday meal at 4:00 P.M. The 6-pound roast has to bake in the oven 20 minutes for every pound and must cool for 15 minutes before serving. What is the latest time she can start baking the roast? (Lesson 1-1)

a. Do you have all of the information necessary to solve this problem?

25a. _____

b. Use the four-step plan to solve the problem.

25b. _____

c. Does your answer make sense? Explain.

25c. _____

Lesson 1-1

NAME _____ DATE _____ PERIOD _____

1-1 Lesson Reading Guide
A Plan for Problem Solving

Get Ready for the Lesson

Read the introduction at the top of page 25 in your textbook. Write your answers below.

1. Do you have all of the information necessary to solve this problem? **See students' work.**

2. Explain how you would solve this problem. Then solve it. **Sample answer: I would add the number of wins.**
$44 + 14 + 8 + 7 + 7 = 80$

3. Does your answer make sense? Explain. **Sample answer: I can compare my answer to the estimate of $40 + 10 + 10 + 10 + 10$ or 80. Since the answer is the exact value of the estimate, the total of 80 makes sense.**

4. What can you do if your first attempt at solving the problem does not work? **Sample answer: I would start over and make a new plan. Then, I would try to solve the problem again. If my answer is not close to the estimate, I would check my arithmetic.**

Read the Lesson

5. In which step of the four-step plan do you decide which strategy you will use to solve the problem? **Plan**

6. What does the four-step plan suggest you do if your answer is not correct? **Make a new plan and start again.**

7. Complete the sentence: Once you solve a problem, make sure your solution contains any appropriate _____. **units or labels**

Remember What You Learned

8. Think of a way to help you remember the names of each of the steps of the four-step plan in the correct order. For example, try writing a sentence using all of the words. **See students' work.**

Chapter Resources

NAME _____ DATE _____ PERIOD _____

1 Anticipation Guide
Introduction to Algebra and Functions

Step 1 *Before you begin Chapter 1*

- Read each statement.
- Decide whether you Agree (A) or Disagree (D) with the statement.
- Write A or D in the first column OR if you are not sure whether you agree or disagree, write NS (Not Sure).

STEP 1 A, D, or NS	Statement	STEP 2 A or D
	1. When solving math problems, all the information given in the problem should be used.	D
	2. The exponent of 4 is 1.	A
	3. Numbers written with exponents are in exponential form.	A
	4. The square of a number is found by finding a factor that multiplied by itself will equal the number.	D
	5. The number 24 is a perfect square.	D
	6. All operations within grouping symbols should be evaluated first in an expression.	A
	7. The expression $(3 + 1)^2$ is equal to $3^2 + 1^2$.	D
	8. The expression $8n + 4n - 6$ contains two terms.	D
	9. The solution to an equation is any number that makes the equation true.	A
	10. An example of the Identity Property of Multiplication is $6 \times 9 = 9 \times 6$.	D
	11. In an arithmetic sequence, each term is found by adding the same number to the previous term.	A
	12. A function table is a way to organize the input and output numbers of a function.	A

Step 2 *After you complete Chapter 1*

- Reread each statement and complete the last column by entering an A (Agree) or a D (Disagree).
- Did any of your opinions about the statements change from the first column?
- For those statements that you mark with a D, use a separate sheet of paper to explain why you disagree. Use examples, if possible.

NAME _____ DATE _____ PERIOD _____

1-1 Skills Practice

A Plan for Problem Solving

Answer these questions about the four-step problem-solving plan.

1. During which step do you ask if your answer makes sense?
Check

2. During which step do you revise or make a new plan if your first plan doesn't work?
Check

3. During which step do you select a strategy for solving the problem?
Step 2: Plan

4. During which step do you ask yourself, "What do I need to find out?"
Step 1: Understand

Choose one of the following to describe how you would plan to solve each problem. Do not solve the problems.

A. Use only one operation, such as addition or multiplication.

B. Use a combination of operations, such as division and addition.

C. Use a different strategy.

5. **MONEY** Julia opened a savings account with a deposit of $36. She then deposited $5 per week for one month. If she then withdrew $9.50, how much is left in her savings account? **B**

6. In how many different patterns can 3 rose bushes, 2 sunflowers, and 5 tulip plants be planted in a garden? **C**

7. Use the four-step plan to solve Exercise 5.

A. Understand
I need to find how much is left in the savings account. First, I need to find the total deposits.

B. Plan
Find the total deposits. Add them to the first deposit, then subtract the withdrawal.

C. Solve
Since there are 4 weeks in a month, the total deposits are $4 \times 5 = 20$. $36 + 20 = 56$. Subtract $9.50. 56 - 9.50 = $46.50.

D. Check
The difference between the deposits and withdrawal is about $10. This means the account should be about $10 more than $36, so the answer is reasonable.

Chapter 1   11   Course 2

NAME _____ DATE _____ PERIOD _____

1-1 Study Guide and Intervention

A Plan for Problem Solving

Four-Step Problem-Solving Plan

When solving problems, it is helpful to have an organized plan to solve the problem. The following four steps can be used to solve any math problem.

1. **Understand** – Get a general understanding of the problem. What information is given?
2. **Plan** – Select a strategy to solve the problem and estimate the answer.
3. **Solve** – Carry out your plan to solve the problem.
4. **Check** – Determine the reasonableness of your answer compared to your estimate.

Example 1 Use the four-step plan to solve the problem.

RECREATION A canoe rental store along the Illinois River in Oklahoma has 30 canoes that it rents on a daily basis during the summer season. If canoes rent for $15 per day, how much money can the store collect for canoe rentals during the month of July?

Understand You know that they rent 30 canoes per day for $15 each. You need to determine the total amount of money that can be collected during the month of July.

Plan First, find the total amount of money that can be collected each day by finding the product of 30 and 15. Next, multiply the previous result by 31, the number of days in July. You can estimate this result by $30.30 \times 15 \times 30 = 13,500$.

Solve Since $30 \times $15 = 450, the canoe rental store can collect $450 in rental fees each day. This means the total amount of money that could be collected during the month of July is 450×31 or $13,950.

Check Is your answer reasonable? The answer is close to the estimate of $13,500.

Exercises

Use the four-step plan to solve each problem.

1. **MONEY** Colin works for his dad during summer vacation. His dad pays him $5.20 per hour and he works 20 hours per week. How much will Colin earn during his 8-week summer vacation? **$832.00**

2. **BOOKS** A student assistant in the school library is asked to shelve 33 books. If he puts away 9 books the first hour and then 6 books each hour after that, how long will it take him to shelve all 33 books? **5 hours**

3. **SHOPPING** Alicia bought a $48 sweater on sale for $25 and a $36 purse on sale for $22. How much did Alicia save? **$37**

4. **MAIL** It cost Ramon $3.73 to mail a package to his grandmother. The post office charged $2.38 for the first pound and 45 cents for each additional pound. How much did the package weigh? **4 pounds**

Chapter 1   10   Course 2

A2

Lesson 1-1

NAME _____ DATE _____ PERIOD _____

1-1 Practice
A Plan for Problem Solving

Use the four-step plan to solve each problem.

1. **ENGINES** A car engine turns 900 revolutions per minute while idling. How many revolutions does a car engine turn in one second while idling? **15 revolutions in one second**

2. **DISTANCE** While traveling in Montana from Butte to Sidney, Mr. Kowalski, recorded that the distance from Butte to Sidney was about 6 times the distance from Butte to Bozeman. Bozeman lies between Butte and Sidney. If the distance from Butte to Bozeman is 82 miles, what is the approximate distance from Bozeman to Sidney? **410 miles**

3. **NUMBERS** What are the next two numbers in the pattern?
3.1, 3.11, 33.11, 33.111, _____ , _____ **333.111, 333.1111**

4. **TIDES** The Bay of Fundy in Nova Scotia, Canada is known for large tides. On a particular day low tide was at 2.3 feet. The tide then rose 6.6 feet every hour for the next six hours. What was the height of high tide on that particular day? **41.9 feet**

5. **BASKETBALL** If team A won by 2 points what was the number of points scored by team A in the 3rd quarter? **25 points**

| Team | Quarter Scores | | | | Final |
	1st	2nd	3rd	4th	Score
A	21	18	?	17	?
B	15	19	20	25	79

6. **COOKING** A cake recipe requires a total 16 tablespoons of butter for one cake, some for the batter and some for the frosting. If 4 tablespoons of butter are needed for the batter for one cake, how many tablespoons of butter are needed for the frosting if Samantha wants to bake three cakes? **36 tablespoons**

NAME _____ DATE _____ PERIOD _____

1-1 Word Problem Practice
A Plan for Problem Solving

MAGAZINES For Exercises 1 and 2, use the table that shows the costs of several popular magazines.

| Costs of Popular Magazines | | |
Magazine	Cost of Yearly Subscription	Cost of a Single Copy
Teen World	$9.98 (12 issues)	$3.25
Soccer World	$19.97 (6 issues)	$4.99
Book Nation	$19.98 (12 issues)	$2.99
TV Weekly	$46.28 (52 issues)	$1.95

1. How much could you save by buying Teen World with a yearly subscription rather than 12 single copies? **$29.02**

2. Which of the magazines saves you the most money by purchasing a yearly subscription instead of an equivalent number of single copies? How much will you save? **TV Weekly; $55.12**

3. **BICYCLING** Adriana can ride her bicycle 6 miles in one hour. How long will it take her to ride 15 miles? **2.5 h**

4. **BASKETBALL** At Johnson Middle School an average of 500 people attended each of the 15 home basketball games. If admission was $3 per person, about how much money was collected in all? **$22,500**

5. **THEATER** A local theater has floor seating, balcony seating, and box seating. If the theater contains 2,500 seats with 425 seats in the balcony and 215 box seats, how many seats are on the floor? **1,860 seats**

6. **POPCORN** Janelle plans to buy three boxes of popcorn at the movies for herself and two friends. If each box costs $1.95, how much change will she receive when she pays with a ten-dollar bill? **$4.15**

Answers (Lessons 1-1 and 1-2)

1-2 Lesson Reading Guide
Powers and Exponents

NAME _____ DATE _____ PERIOD _____

Get Ready for the Lesson

Read the introduction at the top of page 30 in your textbook. Write your answers below.

1. How is doubling shown in the table? **multiplying by 2**

2. How many text messages will be sent after 4 minutes? **16**

3. What is the relationship between the number of 2s and the number of minutes? **There is one 2 for every minute.**

Read the Lesson

4. What is the difference between a power and an exponent? An exponent tells how many times the base is used as a factor, and a power is a number expressed using an exponent.

5. Identify the exponent in each expression.

a. 5^8 **8**

b. 8^5 **5**

c. 8^3 **3**

d. 8 **1**

6. Complete the sentence:
Numbers written with exponents are in _____ form, whereas numbers written without exponents are in _____ form.
exponential; standard

Remember What You Learned

7. In the expression 6^7, circle the exponent in red. Then circle the power in another color. **See students' work.**

Chapter 1   15   Course 2

1-1 Enrichment
The Great State Mystery

NAME _____ DATE _____ PERIOD _____

The United States of America has not always had 50 states. The states gradually joined the Union, starting with the first state in 1787 to the most recent state in 1959. The tables lists 15 states and their populations based on the 2000 Census. Use the 6 clues given and a problem solving process to complete the table below.

Delaware	783,600	Iowa	2,926,324	New York	18,976,457
Georgia	8,186,453	Louisiana	4,468,976	Ohio	11,353,140
Hawaii	1,211,537	Mississippi	2,844,658	Texas	20,851,820
Illinois	12,419,293	New Jersey	8,414,350	Wisconsin	5,363,675
Indiana	6,080,485	New Mexico	1,819,046	Virginia	7,078,515

1. The first state to enter the Union has the least population of the states listed.

2. The states beginning with the letter T were the 19th, 21st, and 29th states admitted to the Union. Iowa entered the Union 30 years after Indiana.

3. New Jersey and Georgia were among the original thirteen colonies. Their entry number is the same as the digit in the hundreds place of their population.

4. Hawaii, Texas, and Wisconsin were the 28th, 30th, and 50th states admitted to the Union, but not in that order. To find their order, put them in order from greatest to least population.

5. The state with the second largest population entered the Union 15 years before Ohio and 24 years before the state with a population in the 4 millions.

6. The day of the month that Mississippi was admitted into the Union can be found by dividing its order of entry by 2.

Order of Entry	State Name	Date of Entry
1	Delaware	December 7, 1787
3	New Jersey	December 18, 1787
4	Georgia	January 2, 1788
10	Virginia	June 25, 1788
11	New York	June 26, 1788
17	Ohio	March 1, **1803**
18	Louisiana	April 30, 1812
19	Indiana	December 11, 1816
20	Mississippi	December **10**, 1817
21	Illinois	December 3, 1818
28	Texas	December 29, 1845
29	Iowa	December 28, 1846
30	Wisconsin	May 29, 1848
47	New Mexico	January 6, 1912
50	Hawaii	August 21, 1959

Chapter 1   14   Course 2

A4

Copyright © Glencoe/McGraw-Hill, a division of The McGraw-Hill Companies, Inc.

1-2 Study Guide and Intervention
Powers and Exponents

$3^4 = 3 \cdot 3 \cdot 3 \cdot 3 = 81$

Base — common factors — Exponent

The **exponent** tells you how many times the **base** is used as a factor.

Example 1 Write 6^3 as a product of the same factor.

The base is 6. The exponent 3 means that 6 is used as a factor 3 times.
$6^3 = 6 \cdot 6 \cdot 6$

Example 2 Evaluate 5^4.

$5^4 = 5 \cdot 5 \cdot 5 \cdot 5$
$= 625$

Example 3 Write $4 \cdot 4 \cdot 4 \cdot 4$ in exponential form.

The base is 4. It is used as a factor 5 times, so the exponent is 5.
$4 \cdot 4 \cdot 4 \cdot 4 \cdot 4 = 4^5$

Exercises

Write each power as a product of the same factor.

1. 7^3 $7 \cdot 7 \cdot 7$
2. 2^7 $2 \cdot 2 \cdot 2 \cdot 2 \cdot 2 \cdot 2 \cdot 2$
3. 9^2 $9 \cdot 9$
4. 15^4 $15 \cdot 15 \cdot 15 \cdot 15$

Evaluate each expression.

5. 3^5 **243**
6. 7^3 **343**
7. 8^4 **4,096**
8. 5^3 **125**

Write each product in exponential form.

9. $2 \cdot 2 \cdot 2 \cdot 2$ 2^4
10. $7 \cdot 7 \cdot 7 \cdot 7 \cdot 7 \cdot 7$ 7^6
11. $10 \cdot 10 \cdot 10$ 10^3
12. $9 \cdot 9 \cdot 9 \cdot 9 \cdot 9$ 9^5
13. $12 \cdot 12 \cdot 12$ 12^3
14. $5 \cdot 5 \cdot 5 \cdot 5$ 5^4
15. $6 \cdot 6 \cdot 6 \cdot 6 \cdot 6$ 6^5
16. $1 \cdot 1 \cdot 1 \cdot 1 \cdot 1 \cdot 1 \cdot 1 \cdot 1$ 1^8

1-2 Skills Practice
Powers and Exponents

Write each power as a product of the same factor.

1. 11^2 $11 \cdot 11$
2. 3^4 $3 \cdot 3 \cdot 3 \cdot 3$
3. 2^5 $2 \cdot 2 \cdot 2 \cdot 2 \cdot 2$
4. 9^3 $9 \cdot 9 \cdot 9$
5. 15^3 $15 \cdot 15 \cdot 15$
6. 4^3 $4 \cdot 4 \cdot 4$
7. 1^6 $1 \cdot 1 \cdot 1 \cdot 1 \cdot 1 \cdot 1$
8. 17^4 $17 \cdot 17 \cdot 17 \cdot 17$
9. 3^7 $3 \cdot 3 \cdot 3 \cdot 3 \cdot 3 \cdot 3 \cdot 3$
10. 8^6 $8 \cdot 8 \cdot 8 \cdot 8 \cdot 8 \cdot 8$

Evaluate each expression.

11. 9^2 **81**
12. 8^2 **64**
13. 8^3 **512**
14. 2^4 **16**
15. 2^5 **32**
16. 6^3 **216**
17. 3^4 **81**
18. 3^5 **243**
19. 9^3 **729**
20. 11^2 **121**
21. 4^7 **16,384**
22. 12^3 **1,728**
23. 1^9 **1**
24. 10^4 **10,000**
25. 20^4 **160,000**
26. 2^6 **64**

Write each product in exponential form.

27. $12 \cdot 12$ 12^2
28. $10 \cdot 10 \cdot 10$ 10^3
29. $4 \cdot 4 \cdot 4 \cdot 4 \cdot 4$ 4^5
30. $9 \cdot 9 \cdot 9 \cdot 9$ 9^4
31. $15 \cdot 15 \cdot 15 \cdot 15 \cdot 15$ 15^5
32. $6 \cdot 6 \cdot 6 \cdot 6 \cdot 6 \cdot 6 \cdot 6 \cdot 6$ 6^8

Lesson 1-2

Answers

1-2 Word Problem Practice

Powers and Exponents

NAME _____ DATE _____ PERIOD _____

1. **SPACE SHUTTLE** The cost of each flight of the Space Shuttle is about $10,000,000. Write this amount in exponential form. **10^7 dollars**

2. **ANIMALS** The African bush elephant is the largest land animal and weighs about 8 tons. Write this amount in exponential form. **2^3 tons**

3. **VOLUME** To find the volume of a rectangular box you multiply the length times the width times the height. In a cube all sides are the same length. If the cube has length, width, and height of 6 inches, write the volume as a product. Then write it in exponential form. **$6 \times 6 \times 6$; 6^3 in^3**

4. **SCIENCE** A certain type of cell doubles every hour. If you start with one cell, at the end of one hour you would have 2 cells, at the end of two hours you have 4 cells, and so on. The expression $2 \times 2 \times 2 \times 2 \times 2$ tells you how many cells you would have after five hours. Write this expression in exponential form; then evaluate it. **2^5 cells; 32 cells**

5. **MATH** Write 625 using exponents in as many ways as you can. **5^4; 25^2**

6. **PREFIXES** Many prefixes are used in mathematics and science. The prefix giga in gigameter represents 1,000,000,000 meters. Write this prefix as a power of ten. **10^9 meters**

7. **LIBRARY** The school library contains 9^4 books. How many library books are in the school library? **6,561 books**

8. **HOT DOGS** The concession stand at the county fair sold 6^3 hot dogs on the first day. How many hot dogs did they sell? **216 hot dogs**

1-2 Practice

Powers and Exponents

NAME _____ DATE _____ PERIOD _____

Write each power as a product of the same factor.

1. 5^7 $5 \cdot 5 \cdot 5 \cdot 5 \cdot 5 \cdot 5 \cdot 5$

2. 2^4 $2 \cdot 2 \cdot 2 \cdot 2$

3. 7^2 $7 \cdot 7$

4. 10^5 $10 \cdot 10 \cdot 10 \cdot 10 \cdot 10$

5. 3^3 $3 \cdot 3 \cdot 3$

6. 6^8 $6 \cdot 6 \cdot 6 \cdot 6 \cdot 6 \cdot 6 \cdot 6 \cdot 6$

7. *four to the eighth power* $4 \cdot 4 \cdot 4 \cdot 4 \cdot 4 \cdot 4 \cdot 4 \cdot 4$

8. *eight cubed* $8 \cdot 8 \cdot 8$

9. *ten squared* $10 \cdot 10$

Write each product in exponential form.

10. $9 \cdot 9 \cdot 9 \cdot 9 \cdot 9$ 9^6

11. $1 \cdot 1 \cdot 1 \cdot 1 \cdot 1$ 1^5

12. $2 \cdot 2 \cdot 2 \cdot 2 \cdot 2 \cdot 2 \cdot 2$ 2^7

13. $6 \cdot 6 \cdot 6 \cdot 6 \cdot 6 \cdot 6$ 6^9

14. $5 \cdot 5$ 5^2

15. $4 \cdot 4 \cdot 4 \cdot 3 \cdot 3 \cdot 3 \cdot 3$ $4^2 \cdot 3^5$

Evaluate each expression.

16. 4^3 **64**

17. 1^{11} **1**

18. 2^5 **32**

19. 10^3 **1,000**

20. 9^3 **729**

21. 8^1 **8**

22. *five to fourth power*   **625**

23. *7 squared*   **49**

24. *zero to the sixth power*   **0**

Use a calculator to determine whether each sentence is *true* or *false*.

25. $2^8 = 8^2$ **false**

26. $17^2 < 172$ **false**

27. $3^2 > 1^{19}$ **true**

Order the following powers from least to greatest.

28. $7^2, 5^3, 3^4, 2^5$ $2^5, 7^2, 3^4, 5^3$

29. $4^3, 11^3, 12^2, 8^3$ $11^3, 4^3, 12^2, 8^3$

30. $3^9, 5^7, 7^5, 9^3$ $9^3, 7^5, 3^9, 5^7$

31. **INTERACTIVE MAPS** Mansi is using an interactive map on her computer that allows her to zoom in or zoom out. Each time she zooms out the scale of the map increases by a power of ten. If she zooms out four times the scale is 10^4 times greater. Write this number in standard form. **$10^4 = 10,000$**

32. **BACTERIA** A lab technician observed 5 bacteria growing in a lab dish. One hour later he observed 25 bacteria. Every hour he notices about 5 times as many as the hour before. After several hours of observation, he determined the lab dish had 5^9 bacteria. Use a calculator to find the number in standard form that represents the bacteria in the lab dish. **$5^9 = 1,953,125$**

Left page

NAME _____ DATE _____ PERIOD _____

1-2 Enrichment
The Four-Digit Problem

Use the digits 1, 2, 3, and 4 to write expressions for the numbers 1 through 50. Each digit is used exactly once in each expression. (There might be more than one expression for a given number.)

You can use addition, subtraction, multiplication (not division), exponents, and parentheses in any way you wish. Also, you can use two digits to make one number, as in 34. A few expressions are given to get you started.
Sample answers given.

$1 = (3 \times 1) - (4 - 2)$

$2 = (4 - 3) + (2 - 1)$

$3 = (4 - 3) + (2 \times 1)$

$4 = (4 - 2) + (3 - 1)$

$5 = (4 - 2) + (3 \times 1)$

$6 = 4 + 3 + 1 - 2$

$7 = 3(4 - 1) - 2$

$8 = 4 + 3 + 2 - 1$

$9 = 4 + 2 + (3 \times 1)$

$10 = 4 + 3 + 2 + 1$

$11 = (4 \times 3) - (2 - 1)$

$12 = (4 \times 3) \times (2 - 1)$

$13 = (4 \times 3) + (2 - 1)$

$14 = (4 \times 3) + (2 \times 1)$

$15 = 2(3 + 4) + 1$

$16 = (4 \times 2) \times (3 - 1)$

$17 = 3(4 + 2) - 1$

$18 = (2 \times 3) \times (4 - 1)$

$19 = 3(2 + 4) + 1$

$20 = 21 - (4 - 3)$

$21 = (4 + 3) \times (2 + 1)$

$22 = 21 + (4 - 3)$

$23 = 31 - (4 \times 2)$

$24 = (4 + 2) \times (3 + 1)$

$25 = (2 + 3) \times (4 + 1)$

$26 = 24 + (3 - 1)$

$27 = 3^2 \times (4 - 1)$

$28 = 21 + 4 + 3$

$29 = 2^{(4 + 1)} - 3$

$30 = (2 \times 3) \times (4 + 1)$

$31 = 34 - (2 + 1)$

$32 = 4^2 \times (3 - 1)$

$33 = 21 + (4 \times 3)$

$34 = 2 \times (14 + 3)$

$35 = 2^{(4 + 1)} + 3$

$36 = 34 + (2 \times 1)$

$37 = 31 + 4 + 2$

$38 = 42 - (1 + 3)$

$39 = 42 - (1 \times 3)$

$40 = 41 - (3 - 2)$

$41 = 43 - (2 \times 1)$

$42 = 43 - (2 - 1)$

$43 = 42 + 1^3$

$44 = 43 + (2 - 1)$

$45 = 43 + (2 \times 1)$

$46 = 43 + (2 + 1)$

$47 = 31 + 4^2$

$48 = 4^2 \times (3 \times 1)$

$49 = 41 + 2^3$

$50 = 41 + 3^2$

Right page

NAME _____ DATE _____ PERIOD _____

1-2 Scientific Calculator Activity
The Power Key

The power key $\boxed{\wedge}$ on a scientific calculator makes it easier to evaluate expressions with exponents.

Example 1 Evaluate 3^5.

Enter: 3 $\boxed{\wedge}$ 5 $\boxed{\text{ENTER}}$ 243

Therefore, $3^5 = 243$.

Example 2 Evaluate $2 \cdot 4^3$.

Enter: 2 $\boxed{\times}$ 4 $\boxed{\wedge}$ 3 $\boxed{\text{ENTER}}$ 128

Therefore, $2 \cdot 4^3 = 128$.

Exercises Evaluate each expression.

1. 2^5 **32**

2. 5^4 **625**

3. 25^4 **390,625**

4. 10^6 **1,000,000**

5. 2^{10} **1,024**

6. 9^7 **4,782,969**

7. $3 \cdot 6^3$ **648**

8. $4^3 \cdot 3^4$ **5,184**

9. $2^5 \cdot 5^4$ **20,000**

10. n^3 if $n = 5$ **125**

11. a^4 if $a = 7$ **2,401**

12. c^7 if $c = 4$ **16,384**

13. $s^2 \cdot s^5$ if $s = 3$ **2,187**

14. $n^3 + n^5$ if $n = 2$ **40**

15. 22 cubed **10,648**

16. **CHALLENGE** What is the greatest power of 2 that the calculator will display before it gives an error message? **Answer will vary depending on calculator.**

Answers

NAME _____ DATE _____ PERIOD _____

1-3 Study Guide and Intervention

Squares and Square Roots

The product of a number and itself is the **square** of the number. Numbers like 4, 25, and 2.25 are called **perfect squares** because they are squares of rational numbers. The factors multiplied to form perfect squares are called **square roots**. Both $5 \cdot 5$ and $(-5)(-5)$ equal 25. So, 25 has two square roots, 5 and -5. A **radical sign**, $\sqrt{}$, is the symbol used to indicate the *positive* square root of a number. So, $\sqrt{25} = 5$.

Examples

1 Find the square of 5.

$5 \cdot 5 = 25$

2 Find the square of 16.

16 $\boxed{x^2}$ $\boxed{\text{ENTER} =}$ **256**

3 Find $\sqrt{49}$.

$7 \cdot 7 = 49$, so $\sqrt{49} = 7$.

4 Find $\sqrt{169}$.

$\boxed{\text{2nd}}$ $\boxed{[\sqrt{}]}$ 169 $\boxed{\text{ENTER} =}$ **13**

So, $\sqrt{169} = 13$.

Example 5 A square tile has an area of 144 square inches. What are the dimensions of the tile?

$\boxed{\text{2nd}}$ $\boxed{[\sqrt{}]}$ 144 $\boxed{\text{ENTER} =}$ **12**   Find the square root of 144.

So, the tile measures 12 inches by 12 inches.

Exercises

Find the square of each number.

1. 2 **4**
2. 9 **81**
3. 14 **196**

4. 15 **225**
5. 21 **441**
6. 45 **2,025**

Find each square root.

7. $\sqrt{16}$ **4**
8. $\sqrt{36}$ **6**
9. $\sqrt{256}$ **16**

10. $\sqrt{1,024}$ **32**
11. $\sqrt{361}$ **19**
12. $\sqrt{484}$ **22**

Chapter 1   23   *Course 2*

NAME _____ DATE _____ PERIOD _____

1-3 Lesson Reading Guide

Squares and Square Roots

Get Ready for the Lesson

Complete the Mini Lab at the top of page 34 in your textbook. Write your answers below.

1. Using tiles, try to construct squares with areas 4, 9, and 16 square units. **See students' work.**

2. Try to construct squares with areas 12, 18, and 20 square units. **See students' work.**

3. Which of the areas for squares? **4, 9, and 16 square units**

4. What is the relationship between the lengths of the sides and the areas of these squares? **The length of the side squared equals the area.**

5. Using your square tiles, create a square that has an area of 49 square units. What are the lengths of the sides of the square? **7 units**

Read the Lesson 6a–c. Sample answers are given.

6. In this lesson, the word *square* is used in several different ways. Tell the meaning of the word as it is used in each phrase or sentence.

a. Find the *square* of 3. **3 times 3**

b. 9 units *squared* **9 square units; 9 squares with sides of 1 unit each**

c. A boxing ring is a *square* with an area of 400 ft². **a rectangle with equal sides**

Remember What You Learned

7. Work with a partner. Use a calculator to find the squares of six numbers, some of them decimals. Then write only the squares in a list and exchange lists with your partner. Find the square roots of the squares in the list that you receive. Write your answers in the form $\sqrt{x} = y$. **See students' work.**

Chapter 1   22   *Course 2*

Answers (Lesson 1-3)

1-3 Practice

Squares and Square Roots

Find the square of each number.

1. 2 **4**
2. 8 **64**
3. 10 **100**

4. 11 **121**
5. 15 **225**
6. 25 **625**

7. What is the square of 5? **25**

8. Find the square of 16. **256**

9. Find the square of 21. **441**

Find each square root.

10. $\sqrt{64}$ **8**
11. $\sqrt{121}$ **11**
12. $\sqrt{169}$ **13**

13. $\sqrt{0}$ **0**
14. $\sqrt{81}$ **9**
15. $\sqrt{289}$ **17**

16. $\sqrt{900}$ **30**
17. $\sqrt{1}$ **1**
18. $\sqrt{484}$ **22**

19. **PACKAGING** An electronics company uses three different sizes of square labels to ship products to customers. The area of each type of label is shown in the table.

Labels	
Type	Area
Priority:	100 cm²
Caution:	225 cm²
Address:	144 cm²

If the length of a side of a square is the square root of the area, what is the length of a side for each label? **Priority: 10 cm; Caution: 15 cm; Address: 12 cm**

20. How much larger is the Caution label than the Address label? **81 cm²**

21. **RECREATION** A square hot tub is outlined by a 2-foot wide tile border. In an overhead view, the area of the hot tub and the border together is 144 square feet. What is the length of one side of the hot tub itself? **8 feet**

1-3 Skills Practice

Squares and Square Roots

Find the square of each number.

1. 3 **9**
2. 22 **484**

3. 25 **625**
4. 24 **576**

5. 35 **1,225**
6. 26 **676**

7. 37 **1,369**
8. 50 **2,500**

Find each square root.

9. $\sqrt{25}$ **5**
10. $\sqrt{100}$ **10**

11. $\sqrt{441}$ **21**
12. $\sqrt{900}$ **30**

13. $\sqrt{961}$ **31**
14. $\sqrt{784}$ **28**

15. $\sqrt{3,600}$ **60**
16. $\sqrt{1,936}$ **44**

17. What is the square of −37? **1,369**

18. Find both square roots of 4,900. **70, −70**

19. Square 7.2. **51.84**
20. Square 4.5. **20.25**

Answers

1-3 Word Problem Practice

Squares and Square Roots

1. FERTILIZER John bought a bag of lawn fertilizer that will cover 400 square feet. What are the dimensions of the largest square plot of lawn that the bag of fertilizer will cover? **20 ft by 20 ft**

2. GEOMETRY The area A of a circle with a radius r in feet is given approximately by the formula $A \approx 3.14 r^2$. What is the approximate area of a circle with a radius of 3 feet? **28.26 ft²**

3. MOTION The time t in seconds for an object dropped from a height of h feet to hit the ground is given by the formula $t = \sqrt{\frac{2h}{32}}$. How long will it take an object dropped from a height of 500 feet to hit the ground? Round to the nearest tenth. **5.6 s**

4. PACKAGING A cardboard envelope for a compact disc is a square with an area of 171.61 square centimeters. What are the dimensions of the envelope? **13.1 cm by 13.1 cm**

5. GEOGRAPHY Refer to the squares below. They represent the approximate areas of California, Alabama, and Nebraska. Find the area of Alabama.

50,625 mi²

6. Use the figure in Exercise 5. How much larger is California than Nebraska? **79,296 mi²**

1-3 Enrichment

The Geometric Mean

The square root of the product of two numbers is called their **geometric mean**. The geometric mean of 12 and 48 is $\sqrt{12 \cdot 48} = \sqrt{576}$ or 24.

Find the geometric mean for each pair of numbers.

1. 2 and 8   **4**

2. 4 and 9   **6**

3. 9 and 16   **12**

4. 16 and 4   **8**

5. 16 and 36   **24**

6. 12 and 3   **6**

7. 18 and 8   **12**

8. 2 and 18   **6**

9. 27 and 12   **18**

Recall the definition of a **geometric sequence**. Each term is found by multiplying the previous term by the same number. A missing term in a geometric sequence equals the geometric mean of the two terms on either side.

Find the missing term in each geometric sequence.

10. 4, 12, ☐ , 108, 324   **36**

11. 10, ☐ , 62.5, 156.25, 390.625   **25**

12. 1, 0.4, ☐ , 0.064, 0.0256   **0.16**

13. 700, 70, 7, 0.7, ☐ , 0.007   **0.07**

14. 6, ☐ , 24   **12**

15. 18, ☐ , 32   **24**

1-4 Lesson Reading Guide

Order of Operations

Get Ready for the Lesson

Read the introduction at the top of page 38 in your textbook. Write your answers below.

1. List the differences between their calculations. **Megan multiplied 4 by 3 and then added 6. Dexter added 6 and 4, and then multiplied the result by 3.**

2. Whose calculations are correct? **Megan**

3. Make a conjecture about what should be the first step in simplifying $6 + 4 \cdot 3$. **Multiply 4 by 3.**

Read the Lesson

4. Why did mathematicians agree on an order of operations? **so that numerical expressions would have only one value**

5. What are three ways to indicate multiplication in a mathematical expression? **×, ·, and parentheses**

Remember What You Learned

6. In your own words, describe the order of operations that is used in finding the value of a mathematical expression.
   1. Do all operations within grouping symbols first.
   2. Evaluate all powers before other operations.
   3. Multiply and divide in order from left to right.
   4. Add and subtract in order from left to right.

1-3 Scientific Calculator Activity

Square Roots

Calculators have a key to square a number. This key is usually labeled x^2. Most calculators can also find the square root of a number. You may have to use the shift key to use this function.

Example 1 Find the square of 84.

Enter: 84 x^2 [ENTER] [=] 7056

$84^2 = 7,056$

Example 2 Find $\sqrt{2,025}$.

Enter: [2nd] [$\sqrt{\ }$] 2025 [ENTER] [=] 45

$\sqrt{2025} = 45$

Exercises

Find the square of each number.

1. 38 **1,444**

2. 51 **2,601**

3. 77 **5,929**

4. 101 **10,201**

5. 28.8 **829.44**

6. 15.5 **240.25**

7. 18.7 **349.69**

8. 9.9 **98.01**

9. 39 **1,521**

10. 1 **1**

11. 8.2 **67.24**

12. 222 **49,284**

Find each square root.

13. $\sqrt{900}$ **30**

14. $\sqrt{289}$ **17**

15. $\sqrt{5,184}$ **72**

16. $\sqrt{1,681}$ **41**

17. $\sqrt{5,476}$ **74**

18. $\sqrt{576}$ **24**

19. $\sqrt{1,024}$ **32**

20. $\sqrt{676}$ **26**

21. $\sqrt{2,704}$ **52**

1-4 Skills Practice
Order of Operations

Evaluate each expression.

1. $9 - 3 + 4$
10

2. $8 + 6 - 5$
9

3. $12 \div 4 + 5$
8

4. $25 \times 2 - 7$
43

5. $36 \div 9(2)$
8

6. $6 + 3(7 - 2)$
21

7. $3 \times 6.2 + 5^2$
43.6

8. $(1 + 11)^2 \div 3$
48

9. $12 - (2 + 8)$
2

10. $15 - 24 \div 4 \cdot 2$
3

11. $(4 + 2) \cdot (7 + 4)$
66

12. $(3 \cdot 18) \div (2 \cdot 9)$
3

13. $24 \div 6 + 4^2$
20

14. $3 \times 8 - (9 - 7)^3$
16

15. $9 + (9 - 8 + 3)^4$
265

16. $3 \times 2^2 + 24 \div 8$
15

17. $(15 \div 3)^2 + 9 \div 3$
28

18. $(52 \div 4) + 5^3$
138

19. 26×10^3
26,000

20. 7.2×10^2
720

21. $5 \times 4^2 - 3 \times 2$
74

22. $24 \div 6 \div 2$
2

23. $13 - (6 - 5)^5$
12

24. $(8 - 3 \times 2) \times 6$
12

25. $(11 \cdot 4 - 10) \div 2$
17

26. $10 \div 2 \times (4 - 3)$
5

27. 1.82×10^5
182,000

28. $35 \div 7 \times 2 - 4$
6

29. $2^5 + 7(9 - 1)$
88

30. $12 + 16 \div (3 + 1)$
16

1-4 Study Guide and Intervention
Order of Operations

Use the **order of operations** to evaluate numerical expressions.

1. Evaluate the expressions inside grouping symbols.
2. Evaluate all powers.
3. Multiply and divide in order from left to right.
4. Add and subtract in order from left to right.

Example 1 Evaluate $(10 - 2) - 4 \cdot 2$.

$(10 - 2) - 4 \cdot 2 = 8 - 4 \cdot 2$ Subtract first since $10 - 2$ is in parentheses.
$= 8 - 8$ Multiply 4 and 2.
$= 0$ Subtract 8 from 8.

Example 2 Evaluate $8 + (1 + 5)^2 \div 4$.

$8 + (1 + 5)^2 \div 4 = 8 + 6^2 \div 4$ First, add 1 and 5 inside the parentheses.
$= 8 + 36 \div 4$ Find the value of 6^2.
$= 8 + 9$ Divide 36 by 4.
$= 17$ Add 8 and 9.

Exercises

Evaluate each expression.

1. $(1 + 7) \times 3$
24

2. $28 - 4 \cdot 7$
0

3. $5 + 4 \cdot 3$
17

4. $(40 \div 5) - 7 + 2$
3

5. $35 \div 7(2)$
10

6. 3×10^3
3,000

7. $45 \div 5 + 36 \div 4$
18

8. $42 \div 6 \times 2 - 9$
5

9. $2 \times 8 - 3^2 + 2$
9

10. $5 \times 2^2 + 32 \div 8$
24

11. $3 \times 6 - (9 - 8)^3$
17

12. 3.5×10^2
350

NAME _____ DATE _____ PERIOD _____

1-4 Practice

Order of Operations

Evaluate each expression.

1. $(2 + 9) \times 4$ **44**

2. $8 - (5 + 2)$ **1**

3. $(15 \div 3) + 7$ **12**

4. $(14 + 7) \div 7$ **3**

5. $5 \cdot 6 - 12 \div 4$ **27**

6. $8 \div 2 + 8 - 2$ **10**

7. $16 - 8 \div 2 + 5$ **17**

8. $15 - 3 \cdot 5 + 7$ **7**

9. 7×10^3 **7,000**

10. $2 \times 5^2 + 6$ **56**

11. $7 \cdot 2^3 - 9$ **47**

12. $27 \div 3 \times 2 + 4^2$ **34**

13. $6^3 - 12 \times 4 \cdot 3$ **72**

14. $(15 - 3) \div (8 + 4)$ **1**

15. $(9 - 4) \cdot (7 - 7)$ **0**

16. $8 + 3(5 + 2) - 7 \cdot 2$ **15**

17. $5(6 - 1) - 4 \cdot 6 \div 3$ **17**

18. $(5 + 7)^2 \div 12$ **12**

19. $12 \div (8 - 6)^2$ **3**

20. $(7 + 2)^2 \div 3^2$ **9**

21. $(11 - 9)^2 \cdot (8 - 5)^2$ **36**

22. $64 \div 8 - 3(4 - 3) + 2$ **7**

23. $8 \times 5.1 - (4.1 + 1.4) + 7.1$ **42.4**

For Exercises 24 and 25, write an expression for each situation. Then evaluate the expression to find the solution.

24. **LAWN AREA** The Solomons need to find the area of their front and side yards since they want to reseed the lawn. Both side yards measure 3 meters by 10 meters, while the front yard is a square with a side of 9 meters. They do not need to reseed a portion of the front yard covering 16 square meters where a flower bed is located. What is the area of the yard that the Solomons want to reseed?

$2(3 \times 10) + 9^2 - 16 = 125$; **The area is 125 m².**

25. **COMMUNITY SERVICE** Jariah volunteers at the hospital during the week. She volunteers 3 hours on Monday and Thursday, 4 hours on Saturday and Sunday, and 2 hours on Tuesday. How many hours does Jariah volunteer at the hospital during the week?

$2 \cdot 3 + 2 \cdot 4 + 2 = 16$; **Jariah volunteers 16 hours a week.**

Chapter 1   32   *Course 2*

NAME _____ DATE _____ PERIOD _____

1-4 Word Problem Practice

Order of Operations

1. **FOOTBALL** The middle school team scored three field goals worth three points each and two touchdowns with extra points worth seven points each. Write a numerical expression to find the team's score. Then evaluate the expression. $3(3) + 2(7)$; **23 points**

2. **BOOKS** Juan goes to the school book fair where paperback books are $1.50 and hardback books are $3.00. Juan buys 5 paperback and 2 hardback books. Write a numerical expression to find how much Juan paid for the books. Then evaluate the expression. $5(1.5) + 2(3)$; **$13.50**

3. **GEOMETRY** The perimeter of a hexagon is found by adding the lengths of all six sides of the hexagon. For the hexagon below write a numerical expression to find the perimeter. Then evaluate the expression. $4(5) + 2(8)$; **36**

4. **MONEY** Aisha bought school supplies consisting of 6 spiral notebooks costing $0.39 each, 2 packages of pencils at $0.79 each, and a 3-ring binder for $1.99. Write an expression to find the total amount Aisha spent on school supplies. Then evaluate the expression. $6 \times 0.39 + 2 \times 0.79 + 1.99$; **$5.91**

5. **REASONING** Use the order of operations and the digits 2, 4, 6, and 8 to create an expression with a value of 2. **Sample answer:** $4^2 - (8 + 6)$

6. **NUMBER SENSE** Without parentheses, the expression $8 + 30 \div 2 + 4$ equals 27. Place parentheses in the expression so that it equals 13; then 23. $8 + 30 \div (2 + 4)$; $(8 + 30) \div 2 + 4$

7. **MONEY** Tyrone bought 5 postcards at $0.55 each and a set of postcards for $1.20. Write an expression to find the total amount Tyrone spent on postcards. Then evaluate the expression. $5(0.55) + 1.2$; **$3.95**

8. **DINING** Mr. Firewalks took his family out to eat. They ordered 3 meals costing $8.99 each, 2 sodas at $1.50 each, and 1 glass of tea for $1.25. Write an expression to find the total amount the Firewalks family spent on dinner before taxes and tip. Then evaluate the expression. $3(8.99) + 2(1.5) + 1.25$; **$31.22**

Chapter 1   33   *Course 2*

Chapter 1   **A13**   *Course 2*

1-4 Enrichment
Nested Expressions

Nested Expressions

Sometimes more than one set of parentheses are used to group the quantities in an expression. These expressions are said to have "nested" parentheses. The expression below has "nested" parentheses.

$$(4 + (3 \cdot (2 + 3)) + 8) \div 9$$

Expressions with several sets of grouping symbols are clearer if braces such as ( ) or brackets as [ ] are used. Here is the same example written with brackets and braces.

$$[4 + [3 \cdot (2 + 3)] + 8] \div 9$$

To evaluate expressions of this type, work from the inside out.

$$[4 + [3 \cdot (2 + 3)] + 8] \div 9 = [4 + [3 \cdot 5] + 8] \div 9$$
$$= [4 + 15 + 8] \div 9$$
$$= 27 \div 9$$
$$= 3$$

Evaluate each expression.

1. $3 + [(24 \div 8) \cdot 7] - 20$ **4**

2. $[(16 - 7 + 5) \div 2] - 7$ **0**

3. $[2 \cdot (23 - 6) + 14] \div 6$ **8**

4. $50 - [3 \cdot (15 - 5)] + 25$ **45**

5. $12 + [28 - [2 \cdot (11 - 7)] + 3]$ **35**

6. $\{75 \div 3 \cdot [(17 - 9) \div 2]\} \cdot 2$ **174**

7. $20 + \{3 \cdot [6 + (56 \div 8)]\}$ **59**

8. $\{4 + [5 \cdot (12 - 5)] + 15\} \cdot 10$ **540**

9. $\{15 \cdot [(38 - 26) \div 4]\} - 15$ **30**

10. $\{[[34 + (6 \cdot 5)] \div 8] + 40\}$ **48**

1-4 TI-83/84 Plus Activity
Order of Operations

You can use a graphing calculator to evaluate expressions using the order of operations. If an expression does not have parentheses, you can enter it as you read it. The calculator will use the order of operations when finding the solution.

Example 1 $3 + 4 \cdot 5 - 6 \div 2$

Enter: 3 [+] 4 [×] 5 [−] 6 [÷] 2 [ENTER] 20

So, $3 + 4 \cdot 5 - 6 \div 2 = 20$.

If there are parentheses in the expression, you can enter them using the parentheses keys.

Example 2 $4 \cdot (3 + 2) \div (10 - 8)$

Enter: 4 [×] [( ] 3 [+] 2 [ )] [÷] [( ] 10 [−] 8 [ )] [ENTER] 10

So, $4 \cdot (3 + 2) \div (10 - 8) = 10$.

Exercises

Evaluate each expression.

1. $6 + 3 \cdot 4 - 9$ **9**

2. $4 + 28 \div 4 - 18 \div 9$ **9**

3. $6 + (5 \cdot 3)$ **21**

4. $47 - 18 + 6 \cdot (4 + 3)$ **71**

5. $3(16 - 9) + 11$ **32**

6. $24 \div (1 + 3)$ **6**

7. $5(10 - 4) + 6(56 \div 7)$ **78**

8. $6(18 - 9) - 4(3 + 2)$ **34**

Insert parentheses to make each sentence true. Check with your calculator.

9. $14 \div 2 + 5 \cdot 9 \div 3 = 6$
$14 \div (2 + 5) \cdot 9 \div 3 = 6$

10. $57 - 16 - 1 \div 5 = 8$
$(57 - 16 - 1) \div 5 = 8$

11. $3 \cdot 16 - 12 + 4 \cdot 11 - 7 = 28$
$3 \cdot (16 - 12) + 4 \cdot (11 - 7) = 28$

12. $3 + 4 \div 2 + 2 - 1 = 3$
$3 + 4 \div (2 + 2) - 1 = 3$

13. $4 \cdot 6 - 8 + 6 \div 2 = 17$
$4 \cdot 6 - (8 + 6) \div 2 = 17$

14. $40 + 36 \div 4 \cdot 27 - 24 = 57$
$(40 + 36) \div 4 \cdot (27 - 24) = 57$

Answers (Lesson 1-5)

NAME _____ DATE _____ PERIOD _____

1-5 Study Guide and Intervention

Problem-Solving Investigation: Guess and Check

When solving problems, one strategy that is helpful to use is guess and check. Based on the information in the problem, you can make a guess of the solution. Then use computations to check if your guess is correct. You can repeat this process until you find the correct solution.

You can use guess and check, along with the following four-step problem solving plan to solve a problem.

Understand • Read and get a general understanding of the problem.

Plan • Make a plan to solve the problem and estimate the solution.

Solve • Use your plan to solve the problem.

Check • Check the reasonableness of your solution.

Example

VETERINARY SCIENCE **Dr. Miller saw 40 birds and cats in one day. All together the pets he saw had 110 legs. How many of each type of animal did Dr. Miller see in one day?**

Understand You know that Dr. Miller saw 40 birds and cats total. You also know that there were 110 legs in all. You need to find out how many of each type of animal he saw in one day.

Plan Make a guess and check it. Adjust the guess until you get the correct answer.

Solve

Number of birds	Number of cats	Total number of feet
20	20	2(20) + 4(20) = 120
30	10	2(30) + 4(10) = 100
25	15	2(25) + 4(15) = 110

Check 25 birds have 50 feet. 15 cats have 60 feet. Since 50 + 60 is 110, the answer is correct.

Exercise

GEOMETRY In a math class of 26 students, each girl drew a triangle and each boy drew a square. If there were 89 sides in all, how many girls and how many boys were in the class?

15 girls, 11 boys

NAME _____ DATE _____ PERIOD _____

1-5 Skills Practice

Problem-Solving Investigation: Guess and Check

Solve each problem using the guess and check problem-solving strategy.

1. SPORTS Susan made 2-point baskets and 3-point baskets in her last basketball game. All together she scored 9 points. How many of each type of basket did she make?

3, 2-point baskets
1, 3-point basket

2. ENTERTAINMENT Tickets to the local circus cost $3 for children and $5 for adults. There were three times as many children tickets sold as adult tickets. All together the circus made $700. How many children and how many adults bought tickets to the circus?

150 children tickets
50 adult tickets

3. NUMBERS What are the next two numbers in the following sequence?

5, 13, 37, 109, 325, _____, _____

973, 2917

4. MONEY Richard found $2.40 in change while cleaning his couch. He found the same number of quarters, dimes, and nickels. How many of each coin did he find?

6 quarters
6 dimes
6 nickels

Answers

Answers (Lesson 1-5)

1-5 Word Problem Practice

NAME _____ DATE _____ PERIOD _____

Problem-Solving Investigation: Guess and Check

1. Joan and Amber have a combined age of 34. If Amber is 2 years less than twice Joan's age, how old is each person?

Joan is 12

Amber is 22

2. A number is divided by 3. Then 14 is added to the quotient. The result is 33. What is the original number?

57

3. The key club made $192 at their candle sale. They sold round candles for $4 and square candles for $6. If they sold twice as many square candles as round ones, how many of each type of candle did the key club sell?

12 round

24 square

4. Landon has 37 baseball cards. If 4 cards can fit on one page, how many pages does Landon need to buy?

10 pages

5. Rick earns $500 less than three times as much as Jim. If their combined salary is $49,500, how much do they each earn?

Rick earns $37,000.00

Jim earns $12,500.00

6. The square root of a number is subtracted from the sum of the number and 12. The result is 42. What is the original number?

36

Chapter 1   39   *Course 2*

1-5 Practice

NAME _____ DATE _____ PERIOD _____

Problem-Solving Investigation: Guess and Check

Mixed Problem Solving

For Exercises 1 and 2, choose the appropriate method of computation. Then use the method to solve the problem.

1. **NUMBERS** A number is multiplied by 7. Then 5 is added to the product. The result is 33. What is the number?

The number is 4.

2. **FOOD** Mr. Jones paid $23 for food for his family of seven at the ballpark. Everyone had a drink and either one hot dog or one hamburger. How many hamburgers were ordered?

MENU	
ITEM	PRICE
Hot Dog	$2
Hamburger	$3
Drink	$1

2 hamburgers

Use any strategy to solve Exercises 3–6. Some strategies are shown below.

PROBLEM-SOLVING STRATEGIES
• Guess and Check.
• Find a pattern.

3. **PATTERNS** What are the next two "words" in the pattern?

ace, bdf, ceg, dfh, egi, _____ , _____

fhj; gik

4. **GEOMETRY** The area of each square is twice the area of the next smaller square drawn in it. If the area of the smallest square is 3 square centimeters, what is the area of the largest square?

24 cm²

5. **ALGEBRA** What are the next two numbers in the pattern?

32, 28, 24, 20, **16** , **12**

6. **MONEY** Leeann received $60 for her birthday. The money came in $10 bills and $5 bills. If she received 8 bills, how many of each type did she receive?

4 $10 bills and 4 $5 bills

7. **MONEY** Duane has four dimes, half as many nickels as dimes, and three times as many quarters as nickels. How much money does Duane have?

$2.00

8. **LIBRARY** Mr. Shuck, the librarian, counted 157 books checked-in during the day. This number was 8 less than 3 times the number of books checked-out that same day. How many books were checked-out that day?

55 books

Chapter 1   38   *Course 2*

Lesson 1-6

1-6 Study Guide and Intervention

Algebra: Variables and Expressions

To evaluate an algebraic expression you replace each variable with its numerical value, then use the order of operations to simplify.

Example 1 Evaluate $6x - 7$ if $x = 8$.

$6x - 7 = 6(8) - 7$ Replace x with 8.
$= 48 - 7$ Use the order of operations.
$= 41$ Subtract 7 from 48.

Example 2 Evaluate $5m - 3n$ if $m = 6$ and $n = 5$.

$5m - 3n = 5(6) - 3(5)$ Replace m with 6 and n with 5.
$= 30 - 15$ Use the order of operations.
$= 15$ Subtract 15 from 30.

Example 3 Evaluate $\dfrac{ab}{3}$ if $a = 7$ and $b = 6$.

$\dfrac{ab}{3} = \dfrac{(7)(6)}{3}$ Replace a with 7 and b with 6.
$= \dfrac{42}{3}$ The fraction bar is like a grouping symbol.
$= 14$ Divide.

Example 4 Evaluate $x^3 + 4$ if $x = 3$.

$x^3 + 4 = 3^3 + 4$ Replace x with 3.
$= 27 + 4$ Use the order of operations.
$= 31$ Add 27 and 4.

Exercises

Evaluate each expression if $a = 4$, $b = 2$, and $c = 7$.

1. $3ac$ **84**
2. $5b^3$ **40**
3. abc **56**

4. $5 + 6c$ **47**
5. $\dfrac{ab}{8}$ **1**
6. $2a - 3b$ **2**

7. $\dfrac{b^4}{4}$ **4**
8. $c - a$ **3**
9. $20 - bc$ **6**

10. $2bc$ **28**
11. $ac - 3b$ **22**
12. $6a^2$ **96**

13. $7c$ **49**
14. $6a - b$ **22**
15. $ab - c$ **1**

1-6 Lesson Reading Guide

Algebra: Variables and Expressions

Get Ready for the Lesson

Complete the Mini Lab at the top of page 44 in your textbook. Write your answers below.

1. Draw the next three figures in the pattern.

2. Find the number of squares in each figure and record your data in the table below. The first three are completed for you. **6, 7, 8**

Figure	1	2	3	4	5	6
Number of squares	3	4	5			

3. Without drawing the figure, determine how many squares would be in the 10th figure. Check by making a drawing. **12; See students' work.**

4. Find a relationship between the figure and its number of squares. **The number of squares is two more than the figure number.**

Read the Lesson

5. Match the description with the appropriate term.

The number 3 in the expression $3y + 2$.   **c**   a. variable

The entire expression $2v - 1$.   **b**   b. algebraic expression

The z in the expression $z^2 - 21$.   **a**   c. coefficient

Remember What You Learned

6. The expression $\dfrac{1}{3}\pi r \cdot r \cdot h$ represents the volume of a cone where r is the radius of the circular base and h is the height of the figure. Identify the coefficients, variables and constants. **$\dfrac{1}{3}$ is the coefficient, r and h are the variables. π (pi, pronounced "pie") is a constant. It represents the value 3.14159....**

Answers (Lesson 1-6)

1-6 Practice

Algebra: Variables and Expressions

Evaluate each expression if $r = 5$, $s = 2$, $t = 7$, and $u = 1$.

1. $s + 7$ **9**
2. $9 - u$ **8**
3. $3t + 1$ **22**

4. $5r - 4$ **21**
5. $t - s$ **5**
6. $u + r$ **6**

7. $11t - 7$ **70**
8. $6 + 3u$ **9**
9. $4r - 10s$ **0**

10. $3u^2$ **3**
11. $2t^2 - 18$ **80**
12. $r^2 + 8$ **33**

13. $\dfrac{s}{2}$ **1**
14. $\dfrac{30}{r}$ **6**
15. $\dfrac{(3+u)^2}{8}$ **2**

Evaluate each expression if $a = 4.1$, $b = 5.7$, and $c = 0.3$.

16. $a + b - c$ **9.5**
17. $10 - (a + b)$ **0.2**
18. $b - c + 2$ **7.4**

19. **MOON** The expression $\dfrac{w}{6}$ gives the weight of an object on the Moon in pounds with a weight of w pounds on Earth. What is the weight of a space suit on the Moon if the space suit weighs 178.2 pounds on Earth? **29.7 pounds**

20. Complete the table.

Pounds (p)	Ounces ($16p$)
1	16
2	32
3	48
4	64
5	80

1-6 Skills Practice

Algebra: Variables and Expressions

Evaluate each expression if $w = 2$, $x = 3$, $y = 5$, and $z = 6$.

1. $2w$ **4**
2. $y + 5$ **10**
3. $9 - z$ **3**

4. $x + w$ **5**
5. $3 + 4z$ **27**
6. $6y - 5$ **25**

7. y^2 **25**
8. $y - x$ **2**
9. $\dfrac{z}{2}$ **3**

Evaluate each expression if $m = 3$, $n = 7$, and $p = 9$.

10. $m + n$ **10**
11. $12 - 3m$ **3**
12. $5p$ **45**

13. $3.3p$ **29.7**
14. $3.3p + 2$ **31.7**
15. $2p + 3.3$ **21.3**

16. $20 + 2n$ **34**
17. $20 - 2n$ **6**
18. $\dfrac{n}{7}$ **1**

19. n^2 **49**
20. $6m^2$ **54**
21. $\dfrac{p^2}{3}$ **27**

22. $1.1 + n$ **8.1**
23. $p - 8.1$ **0.9**
24. $3.6m$ **10.8**

25. $3n - 2m$ **15**
26. $3m - n$ **2**
27. $2.1n + p$ **23.7**

28. $\dfrac{m^2}{p}$ **1**
29. $\dfrac{2.5m + 2.5}{5}$ **2**
30. $\dfrac{(n+2)^2}{3}$ **27**

Lesson 1-6

NAME _____ DATE _____ PERIOD _____

1-6 Word Problem Practice

Algebra: Variables and Expressions

1. **FIELD TRIP** The seventh grade math classes are going on a field trip. The field trip will cost $7 per student. Write an expression to find the cost of the field trip for s students. What is the total cost if 26 students go on the trip? **7s; $182**

2. **SOCCER** Jason earns $20 per game as a referee in youth soccer games. Write an expression to find how much money Jason will earn for refereeing any number of games. Let n represent the number of games Jason has refereed. How much will he earn for refereeing 6 games? **20n; $120**

3. **PROFIT** The expressions $c - e$, where c stands for the money collected and e stands for the expenses, is used to find the profit from a basketball concession. If $500 was collected and expenses were $150, find the profit for the concession. **$350**

4. **SAVINGS** Kata has a savings account that contains $230. She decides to deposit $5 each month from her monthly earnings for baby-sitting after school. Write an expression to find how much money Kata will have in her savings account after x months. Let x represent the number of months. Then find out how much she will have in her account after 1 year. **5x + 230; $290**

5. **MONEY** Mr. Wilson has $2,500 in his savings account and m dollars in his checking account. Write an expression that describes the total amount that he has in both accounts. **2,500 + m**

6. **ANIMALS** Write an expression to represent the total number of legs on h horses and c chickens. How many legs are there in 5 horses and 6 chickens? **4h + 2c; 32 legs**

7. **T-SHIRTS** The band wants to order T-shirts. The T-shirts cost $15 each plus a shipping fee of $10. Write an expression to find the total cost of c T-shirts. **15c + 10**

8. **TEMPERATURE** The expression $\frac{9}{5}C + 32$, where C stands for temperature in degrees Celsius, is used to convert Celsius to Fahrenheit. If the temperature is 20 degrees Celsius, find the temperature in degrees Fahrenheit. **68°F**

NAME _____ DATE _____ PERIOD _____

1-6 Enrichment

The First Lady of Science

Chinese-American physicist Chien-Shiung Wu (1912–1997) was born in Shanghai, China. At the age of 24, she came to the United States to further her studies in science. She received her doctorate in physics from the University of California, Berkeley in 1940. Dr. Wu became the first female professor at Princeton University and worked on the Manhattan Project during World War II.

Dr. Wu paved the way for many female scientists. She received numerous awards and honors from American and Chinese universities and was the first woman president of the American Physical Society. She was also the first living scientist to have an asteroid named in her honor.

Evaluate each expression for $p = 9$, $q = 5$, $r = 7$, and $x = 8$. The problem letter and the solution form a key to decoding another fact about Dr. Wu shown below.

A. $r + 3$ **10**

C. $10q$ **50**

E. $q + r$ **12**

G. $p + 5$ **14**

H. $6r - x$ **34**

N. $6 + 4x$ **38**

O. $3q + 5p$ **60**

P. $70 - 2p$ **52**

R. $r^2 + 5$ **54**

S. $4q^2 - 3$ **97**

T. $2r^2$ **98**

Y. $8r - 5$ **51**

In Chinese, *Chien-Shiung* means....

S	T	R	O	N	G		H	E	R	O
97	98	54	60	38	14		34	12	54	60

NAME _____ DATE _____ PERIOD _____

1-7 Lesson Reading Guide
Algebra: Equations

Get Ready for the Lesson

Read the introduction at the top of page 49 in your textbook. Write your answers below.

1. Suppose each team played 34 games. How many losses did each team have?

Women's College Volleyball		
Team	Wins	Losses
Bowling Green State University	28	6
Kent State University	13	21
Ohio University	28	6
University of Akron	7	27
University of Buffalo	14	20
Miami University	13	21

Source: Mid-American Conference

2. Write a rule to describe how you found the number of losses.
34 = wins + losses

3. Let w represent the number of wins and ℓ represent the number of losses. Rewrite your rule using numbers, variables, and an equals sign.
Sample answer: $34 = w + \ell$

Read the Lesson

4. Complete the sentence: An equation that contains a variable is neither true nor false until the variable is replaced with a _____. **number**

5. Describe what it means to model a problem. **Sample answer: Write an equation that represents the problem.**

6. What must you do before you write an equation using a variable when modeling a problem? **Define the variable.**

Remember What You Learned

7. Calculating change after buying lunch is a situation that can be modeled with a simple equation. What other daily activities require you to solve an equation? Write down three sample equations. **See students' work.**

NAME _____ DATE _____ PERIOD _____

1-6 Spreadsheet Activity
Evaluating Expressions

You can use a spreadsheet to evaluate expressions.

Example 1 Evaluate $3x - 2$ when $x = -1, -2, 3,$ and 0.

Step 1 Use the first column, enter the x values you want to substitute. For example, enter -1 in cell A1. Push ENTER after each value.

Step 2 In cell B1, enter an equals sign followed by the formula for the expression which is 3*A1 − 2. Push ENTER to get the result. The answer is -5.

Step 3 In the second column, click on the bottom right hand corner of cell B1 and drag it through cell B4 to find the remaining values.

So, the values of the expression are -5, -8, 7, and -2.

Example 2 Evaluate $2m + 6n$ when $m = -\frac{1}{2}$ and $n = \frac{1}{3}$.

Step 1 In cell A1, enter the value for m. In cell B1, enter the value for n.

Step 2 In cell C1, enter an equals sign followed by the formula for the expression which is 2*A1 + 6*B1. Next press ENTER. The answer is 1.

Exercises Use a spreadsheet to evaluate the following expressions when $x = 2$.

1. $3x - 5$ **1**
2. $2x - 1$ **3**
3. $\frac{1}{2}x + 3$ **4**
4. $0.1x - 3$ **-2.8**
5. $x + 2$ **4**
6. $5x$ **10**

Use a spreadsheet to evaluate the following expressions when $m = -1$ and $n = -2$.

7. mn **2**
8. $\frac{n}{m}$ **2**
9. $2m + n$ **-4**
10. $\frac{mn}{2}$ **1**
11. $-2m - 3n$ **8**
12. $\frac{5mn}{2}$ **5**

Answers (Lesson 1-7)

NAME _____ DATE _____ PERIOD _____

1-7 Study Guide and Intervention
Algebra: Equations

- An **equation** is a sentence in mathematics that contains an equals sign, =.
- The **solution** of an equation is the value that when substituted for the variable makes the equation true.

Example 1 Solve $23 + y = 29$ mentally.

$23 + y = 29$ Write the equation.
$23 + 6 = 29$ You know that $23 + 6$ is 29.
$29 = 29$ Simplify.
The solution is 6.

Example 2

TRAVEL On their annual family vacation, the Wilsons travel 790 miles in two days. If on the first day they travel 490 miles, how many miles must they drive on the second day to reach their destination?

The total distance to travel in two days is 790 miles.

Let m represent the distance to travel on day two.

$m + 490 = 790$

$m + 490 = 790$ Write the equation.
$300 + 490 = 790$ Replace m with 300 to make the equation true.
$790 = 790$ Simplify.

The number 300 is the solution. The distance the Wilsons must travel on day two is 300 miles.

Exercises

Solve each equation mentally.

1. $k + 7 = 15$ **8**

2. $g - 8 = 20$ **28**

3. $6y = 24$ **4**

4. $\frac{a}{3} = 9$ **27**

5. $\frac{x}{6} = 9$ **54**

6. $8 + r = 24$ **16**

7. $12 \cdot 8 = h$ **96**

8. $n \div 11 = 8$ **88**

9. $48 \div 12 = x$ **4**

10. $h - 12 = 24$ **36**

11. $19 + y = 28$ **9**

12. $9f = 90$ **10**

Define a variable. Then write and solve an equation.

13. **MONEY** Aaron wants to buy a video game. The game costs $15.50. He has $10.00 saved from his weekly allowance. How much money does he need to borrow from his mother in order to buy the video game? **M = the amount of money he needs to borrow; M + 10 = 15.5; $5.50**

Chapter 1   48   *Course 2*

NAME _____ DATE _____ PERIOD _____

1-7 Skills Practice
Algebra: Equations

Solve each equation mentally.

1. $a + 7 = 16$ **9**

2. $12 + x = 21$ **9**

3. $4d = 60$ **15**

4. $15 = \frac{u}{3}$ **45**

5. $\frac{b}{7} = 12$ **84**

6. $13 \cdot 3 = y$ **39**

7. $8 + r = 17$ **9**

8. $27 - 12 = m$ **15**

9. $h - 22 = 67$ **89**

10. $27 + 15 = n$ **42**

11. $36 + a = 96$ **60**

12. $99 \div d = 3$ **33**

13. $6t = 66$ **11**

14. $25 = y \div 4$ **100**

15. $b - 25 = 120$ **145**

16. $n \div 5 = 10$ **50**

17. $4y = 48$ **12**

18. $5t = 40$ **8**

19. $50 \cdot d = 150$ **3**

20. $w + 61 = 65$ **4**

21. $88 \div k = 2$ **44**

Graph the solution of each equation on a number line.

22. $v - 6 = 30$ **36**

23. $3a = 27$ **9**

24. $n + 7 = 14$ **7**

See students' work for graphs.

Define a variable. Write an equation and solve.

25. **BAKING** Judy wants to buy some cookies for her birthday party. Cookies come in packages of 6. If she is inviting 24 friends to her party, how many packages of cookies does she need to buy so that each of her friends can have one cookie each?

P = the number of packages of cookies; 6p = 24; 4 packages

Chapter 1   49   *Course 2*

Chapter 1   **A21**   *Course 2*

1-7 Practice
Algebra: Equations

NAME _____ DATE _____ PERIOD _____

Solve each equation mentally.

1. $a + 5 = 14$ **9**
2. $7 + y = 24$ **17**
3. $t - 13 = 33$ **46**
4. $b - 17 = 11$ **28**
5. $12 - r = 0$ **12**
6. $x + 18 = 59$ **41**
7. $63 = 9g$ **7**
8. $8d = 96$ **12**
9. $n = \frac{42}{7}$ **6**
10. $9 = \frac{z}{7}$ **63**
11. $10 = h \div 4$ **40**
12. $55 \div m = 11$ **5**
13. $1.2 + k = 3.0$ **1.8**
14. $2.7 = f - 1.1$ **3.8**
15. $v - 0.5 = 0.2$ **0.7**
16. $12.6 - c = 7.0$ **5.6**
17. $8.8 + j = 18.7$ **9.9**
18. $w + 13.5 = 16.0$ **2.5**

19. **WEATHER** The temperature was 78°F. A cold front moved in, and the temperature dropped to 54°F. Solve the equation $78 - d = 54$ to find the drop in temperature.

   24°F

20. **HOBBIES** Elissa can cut out the pieces of cloth to make four pillows in one hour. Solve the equation $4h = 20$ to find how many hours Elissa needs to cut cloth for 20 pillows.

   5 hours

21. **BOWLING** Jean Conrad is an amateur bowler with an average score of 187. She recently bowled a perfect 300 score. Write an equation that can be used to find how much the perfect score was above her average score and then solve the equation.

   $300 - n = 187$ **or** $n = 300 - 187; n = 113$
   The perfect score of 300 is 113 above her average.

1-7 Word Problem Practice
Algebra: Equations

NAME _____ DATE _____ PERIOD _____

1. **GAS MILEAGE** Mr. Moseley's car has a 20-gallon gas tank. It took 14 gallons of gas to fill his tank. Use the equation $14 + g = 20$ to find the number of gallons g that he had before he filled his tank with gas.   **6 gal**

2. **PAINTING** Latisha earned $5 an hour painting for her dad. If she made $40 last week, use $5h = 40$ to find how many hours h she painted.   **8 h**

3. **LUMBER** Mrs. Garcia had a piece of board that was 15 feet long. She cut off 6.5 feet. Use the equation $6.5 + \ell = 15$ to determine how much of the board ℓ she has left.   **8.5 ft**

4. **MAGAZINES** Mahpee was selling magazine subscriptions. He earned $5 plus $0.50 for each subscription he sold. If Mahpee earned $25, use the equation $25 = 5 + 0.50n$ to find the number of subscriptions n he sold.   **40 subscriptions**

5. **TIRES** The cost of a car tire is $45 plus $10 per order regardless of the number of tires purchased. If Mrs. Sato places an order for $190, use the equation $45t + 10 = 190$ to find the number of tires t she purchased.   **4 tires**

6. **AREA** If the area of a rectangle is 30 square centimeters and the length is 6 centimeters, use the equation $30 = 6w$ to find the width w of the rectangle.   **5 cm**

7. **SUPPLIES** The Jones Middle School had $4,000 to spend on office supplies. They had already spent $1,250. Use the equation $1,250 + d = 4,000$ to find how much money d the school had left for other supplies.   **$2,750**

8. **PENCILS** Mi-Leng spent 90 cents on 6 pencils. Use the equation $90 = 6c$ to find the cost c of each pencil.   **15 cents or $0.15**

Lesson 1-8

NAME _____ DATE _____ PERIOD _____

1-8 Lesson Reading Guide
Algebra: Properties

Get Ready for the Lesson

Read the introduction at the top of page 53 in your textbook. Write your answers below.

1. Find the total cost of admission and a movie ticket for a 4-person family.
   $80

2. Describe the method you used to find the total cost.
   See students' work.

Read the Lesson

3. Describe what is meant by *equivalent expressions*. **Equivalent expressions are expressions that have the same value.**

4. The Identity Property says that adding _____ to a number results in the number and multiplying _____ by a number is the number.
   zero; one

Remember What You Learned

5. Why are the Distributive Property, Commutative Property, Associative Property, and Identity Property called properties? **because they are true for any number**

   Use a dictionary to find the meanings of *distribute* and *commute* that apply to mathematics. Then write an explanation of why the Distributive Property and Commutative Property are named that way.
   Sample answer:
   Distribute means to divide among several. The Distributive Property shows that when a sum is multiplied by a number, when the number is distributed and multiplied by each addend the result is the same. Commute means to move. The Commutative Property shows that when two numbers are added or multiplied the numbers can move around the operation symbol and the result is the same.

Chapter 1   53   *Course 2*

NAME _____ DATE _____ PERIOD _____

1-7 Enrichment
Equations as Models

Equations as Models

When you write an equation that represents the information in a problem, the equation serves as a model for the problem. One equation can be a model for several different problems.

Each of Exercises 1–8 can be modeled by one of these equations.

$n + 2 = 10$ $n - 2 = 10$ $2n = 10$ $\dfrac{n}{2} = 10$

Choose the correct equation. Then solve the problem.

1. Chum earned $10 for working two hours. How much did he earn per hour? **$2n = 10$; $5**

2. Ana needs $2 more to buy a $10 scarf. How much money does she already have? **$n + 2 = 10$; $8**

3. Kathy and her brother won a contest and shared the prize equally. Each received $10. What was the amount of the prize? **$\dfrac{n}{2} = 10$; $20**

4. Jameel loaned two tapes to a friend. He has ten tapes left. How many tapes did Jameel originally have? **$n - 2 = 10$; 12 tapes**

5. In the figure below, the length of $\overline{AC}$ is 10 cm. The length of $\overline{BC}$ is 2 cm. What is the length of $\overline{AB}$?

   A _____ B __ C

   $n + 2 = 10$; 8 cm

6. Ray $\overline{AC}$ bisects $\angle BAD$. The measure of $\angle BAC$ is 10°. What is the measure of $\angle BAD$?

   $\dfrac{n}{2} = 10$; 20°

7. The width of the rectangle below is 2 inches less than the length. What is the length?

   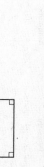

   10 in.

   $n - 2 = 10$; 12 in.

8. In the triangle below, the length of $\overline{PQ}$ is twice the length of $\overline{QR}$. What is the length of $\overline{QR}$?

   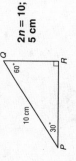

   $2n = 10$; 5 cm

9. **CHALLENGE** On a separate sheet of paper, write a problem that can be modeled by the equation $3a + 5 = 29$. **Answers will vary.**

Chapter 1   52   *Course 2*

Lesson 1-8

1-8 Skills Practice

Algebra: Properties

Use the Distributive Property to write each expression as an equivalent expression. Then evaluate the expression.

1. $3(5 + 1)$ **$3(5) + 3(1)$; 18**

2. $(2 + 7)5$ **$2(5) + 7(5)$; 45**

3. $(10 + 2)7$ **$10(7) + 2(7)$; 84**

4. $2(9 - 8)$ **$2(9) - 2(8)$; 2**

5. $4(10 - 2)$ **$4(10) - 4(2)$; 32**

6. $6(13 + 4)$ **$6(13) + 6(4)$; 102**

Name the property shown by each statement.

7. $2 \times (3 \times 7) = (2 \times 3) \times 7$
Associative Property ($\times$)

8. $6 + 3 = 3 + 6$
Commutative Property (+)

9. $3(9 - 7) = 3(9) - 3(7)$
Distributive Property

10. $18 \times 1 = 18$
Identity Property ($\times$)

11. $7 \times 2 = 2 \times 7$
Commutative Property ($\times$)

12. $6 + (1 + 4) = (6 + 1) + 4$
Associative Property (+)

13. $7 + 0 = 7$
Identity Property (+)

14. $0 + 12 = 12$
Identity Property (+)

15. $625 + 281 = 281 + 625$
Commutative Property (+)

16. $(12 \times 18) \times 5 = 12 \times (18 \times 5)$
Associative Property ($\times$)

17. $2(8 + 2) = 2(8) + 2(2)$
Distributive Property

18. $(15 + 11) + 9 = 15 + (11 + 9)$
Associative Property (+)

19. $(6 + r) + s = 6 + (r + s)$
Associative Property (+)

20. $(4 \times 8) \times a = 4 \times (8 \times a)$
Associative Property ($\times$)

21. $p \times 1 = p$
Identity Property ($\times$)

22. $a + 5 = 5 + a$
Commutative Property (+)

23. $y \times 3 = 3 \times y$
Commutative Property ($\times$)

24. $b + 0 = b$
Identity Property (+)

25. $(x + y) + z = x + (y + z)$
Associative Property (+)

26. $6(200 + 50) = 6(200) + 6(50)$
Distributive Property

1-8 Study Guide and Intervention

Algebra: Properties

Property	Arithmetic	Algebra
Distributive Property	$5(3 + 4) = 5(3) + 5(4)$	$a(b + c) = a(b) + a(c)$
Commutative Property of Addition	$5 + 3 = 3 + 5$	$a + b = b + a$
Commutative Property of Multiplication	$5 \times 3 = 3 \times 5$	$a \times b = b \times a$
Associative Property of Addition	$(2 + 3) + 4 = 2 + (3 + 4)$	$(a + b) + c = a + (b + c)$
Associative Property of Multiplication	$(4 \times 5) \times 6 = 4 \times (5 \times 6)$	$(a \times b) \times c = a \times (b \times c)$
Identity Property of Addition	$5 + 0 = 5$	$a + 0 = a$
Identity Property of Multiplication	$5 \times 1 = 5$	$a \times 1 = a$

Example 1 Use the Distributive Property to write $6(4 + 3)$ as an equivalent expression. Then evaluate the expression.

$6(4 + 3) = 6 \cdot 4 + 6 \cdot 3$ Apply the Distributive Property.
$= 24 + 18$ Multiply.
$= 42$ Add.

Example 2 Name the property shown by each statement.

$5 \times 4 = 4 \times 5$ Commutative Property of Multiplication
$12 + 0 = 12$ Identity Property of Addition
$7 + (6 + 3) = (7 + 6) + 3$ Associative Property of Addition

Exercises

Use the Distributive Property to write each expression as an equivalent expression. Then evaluate the expression.

1. $5(7 + 2)$ **$5(7) + 5(2)$; 45**
2. $4(9 + 1)$ **$4(9) + 4(1)$; 40**
3. $2(6 + 7)$ **$2(6) + 2(7)$; 26**

Name the property shown by each statement.

4. $9 \times 1 = 9$
Identity Property ($\times$)

5. $7 \times 3 = 3 \times 7$
Commutative Property ($\times$)

6. $(7 + 8) + 2 = 7 + (8 + 2)$
Associative Property (+)

7. $6(3 + 2) = 6(3) + 6(2)$
Distributive Property

8. $15 + 12 = 12 + 15$
Commutative Property (+)

9. $1 \times 20 = 20$
Identity Property ($\times$)

10. $(9 \times 5) \times 2 = 9 \times (5 \times 2)$
Associative Property ($\times$)

11. $3 = 0 + 3$
Identity Property (+)

1-8 Practice

Algebra: Properties

Use the Distributive Property to evaluate each expression.

1. $4(5 + 7)$
$4(5) + 4(7) = 48$

2. $6(3 + 1)$
$6(3) + 6(1) = 24$

3. $(10 + 8)2$
$(10)2 + (8)2 = 36$

4. $5(8 - 3)$
$5(8) - 5(3) = 25$

5. $7(4 - 1)$
$7(4) - 7(1) = 21$

6. $(9 - 2)3$
$(9)3 - (2)3 = 21$

Name the property shown by each statement.

7. $7 + (6 + t) = (7 + 6) + t$ **Associative Property (+)**

8. $23 \cdot 15 = 15 \cdot 23$ **Commutative Property (×)**

9. $0 + x = x$ **Identity Property (+)**

10. $3(g + 7) = 3 \cdot g + 3 \cdot 7$ **Distributive Property**

11. $8 \cdot 1 = 8$ **Identity Property (×)**

12. $y + 11 = 11 + y$ **Commutative Property (+)**

13. $5(w + 1) = (w + 1)5$ **Commutative Property (×)**

14. $(4 \cdot d) \cdot 1 = 4 \cdot (d \cdot 1)$ **Associative Property (×)**

15. $(6 + 2)7 = (6)7 + (2)7$ **Distributive Property**

Use one or more properties to rewrite each expression as an equivalent expression that does not use parentheses.

16. $(b + 3) + 6$ **$b + 9$**

17. $7(5x)$ **$35x$**

18. $4(a + 4)$ **$4a + 16$**

19. $7 + (3 + t)$ **$10 + t$**

20. $(2z)0$ **0**

21. $(9 + k)5$ **$45 + 5k$**

22. $8(y - 5) + y$ **$9y - 40$**

23. $(h + 2)3 - 2h$ **$h + 6$**

24. **GROCERY** A grocery store sells an imported specialty cheesecake for $11 and its own store-baked cheesecake for $5. Use the Distributive Property to mentally find the total cost for 6 of each type of cheesecake.
$6(\$5 + \$11) = 6 \cdot \$5 + 6 \cdot \$11 = \$30 + \$66 = \$96$

25. **CHECKING ACCOUNT** Mr. Kenrick balances his checking account statement each month two different ways as shown by the equation, $(b + d) - c = b + (d - c)$, where b is the previous balance, d is the amount of deposits made, and c is the amount of checks written. Name the property that Mr. Kenrick uses to double check his arithmetic.
Associative Property

26. **SPEED** A train is traveling at a speed of 65 miles per hour. The train travels for one hour. What property is used to solve this problem as shown by the statement $65 \cdot 1 = 65$?
Identity Property

1-8 Word Problem Practice

Algebra: Properties

1. **MUSIC** Mr. Escalante and Mrs. Turner plan to take their music classes to a musical revue. Tickets cost $6 each. Mr. Escalante's class needs 22 tickets, and Mrs. Turner's class needs 26 tickets. Use the Distributive Property to write a sentence to express how to find the total cost of tickets in two ways.
$6(22) + 6(26) = 6(22 + 26)$

2. **SAVINGS** Mrs. Perez was looking at her bank account statement. She noticed that her beginning balance was $500, and she had added nothing to her account. What was the ending balance on her statement? What property did you apply? **$500; Identity Property of Addition**

3. **ADDITION** Mr. Brooks was working on addition using dominos with a group of 1st graders. When picking the domino with 3 dots on one end and 5 dots on the other, some students read. "3 plus 5 equal 8" while others read it as "5 plus 3 equals 8." What property were these children using? Explain.
Commutative Property of Addition; the order was different.

4. **AREA** Aleta noticed that for the rectangle below she could either multiply 2 times 3 or 3 times 2 to get its area of 6 square inches. What property allows her to do this?
Commutative Property of Multiplication

3 in. × 2 in.

5. **NUMBER CUBES** Students in Mr. Rivas' class were practicing their multiplication skills by rolling three 6-sided number cubes. Wapi rolled a 2, a 3, and a 5 on his roll. He multiplied the three numbers as follows using the order of operations: $(2 \times 3) \times 5 = 30$. Write another way Wapi could have performed the multiplication without changing the order of the numbers. State the property you used.
$2 \times (3 \times 5) = 30$; Associative Property of Multiplication

6. **FACTS** Bik was working on memorizing her multiplication facts. She noticed that anytime she multiplied a number by 1, she got the same number she started with. What property allows this to be true? **Identity Property of Multiplication**

7. **MONEY** Mei was trying to figure out the cost of 4 boxes of cereal for $2.25 each. Write a sentence to show Mei an easy way to do her calculations. What property did you apply to help her?
$4(2.25) = 4(2.00 + 0.25)$; Distributive Property

8. **WALKING** Jacob walked 3 blocks to Ping's house, then 5 blocks to Jamal's house. Write a sentence to show that the distance from Ping's to Jamal's is the same as the return walk home. Name the property illustrated in your sentence.
$3 + 5 = 5 + 3$; Commutative Property of Addition

Right Page

NAME _____ DATE _____ PERIOD _____

1-8 Scientific Calculator Activity
The Distributive Property

You can solve word problems by using the Distributive Property. The parentheses keys on the calculator will help you.

Example 1

Neil purchased 4 dozen blueberry bagels and 6 dozen cinnamon-raisin bagels for a fund-raiser at school. How many bagels did Neil purchase in all?

Enter: 12 ⊗ ⦅ 4 ⊕ 6 ⦆ ENTER = 120

Neil purchased 120 bagels in all.

Example 2

Jill has been training to run a marathon for 3 weeks. On the first 7 days, she ran 2.5 miles per day. On the next 7 days, she ran 3 miles each day. On each of the last 7 days, she ran 3.75 miles. How many miles in all did Jill run?

Enter: 7 ⊗ ⦅ 2.5 ⊕ 3 ⊕ 3.75 ⦆ ENTER = 64.75

Jill ran 64.75 miles during 3 weeks of training.

Exercises

Solve each problem using the Distributive Property.

1. The company assistant put in an order for supplies that included 15 dozen pens and 8 dozen pencils. How many individual pens and pencils were ordered in all? **276**

2. The Music Source is having a sale on CDs and cassettes. They have 140 CDs and 215 cassettes they are selling for $5.29 each. How much money will they earn if all CDs and cassettes are sold? **$1,877.95**

3. If the Music Source decreased the selling price to $4.95, how much money would they earn? What is the difference in earnings from Exercise 2? **$1,757.25; $120.70**

4. Kevin earns $3.15 per hour for each hour he helps Mr. McCready with lawn work. Kevin worked the following hours: Friday: 3.25 hours; Saturday: 4 hours; Sunday: 2.5 hours. How much money did Kevin earn in all? Round to the nearest cent. **$30.71**

Chapter 1   59   Course 2

Left Page

NAME _____ DATE _____ PERIOD _____

1-8 Enrichment
Name That Property

Name That Property

You know that the Commutative Property applies to the operations of addition and multiplication. You also know that the Associative Property applies to operations of addition and multiplication. What about the other operations? Does the Commutative Property apply to division? Does the Associative Property apply to subtraction? Does the Distributive Property apply to subtraction or division?

Look at these examples to determine if the properties also apply to subtraction or division.

Commutative Property

Subtraction	Division
Try this:	*Try this:*
$5 - 4 \stackrel{?}{=} 4 - 5$	$8 \div 2 \stackrel{?}{=} 2 \div 8$

1. Does the Commutative Property apply to division and subtraction? Explain. **Sample answer: The Commutative Property does not apply to subtraction because $1 \neq -1$. It does not apply to division since $4 \neq 0.25$.**

Associative Property

Subtraction	Division
Try this:	*Try this:*
$7 - (3 - 2) \stackrel{?}{=} (7 - 3) - 2$	$8 \div (4 \div 2) \stackrel{?}{=} (8 \div 4) \div 2$

2. Does the Associative Property apply to subtraction and division? Explain. **Sample answer: The Associative Property does not apply to subtraction because $7 - 1 \neq 4 - 2$. It does not apply to division since $8 \div 2 \neq 2 \div 2$.**

Distributive Property

Subtraction	Division
Try this:	*Try this:*
$3(8 - 2) \stackrel{?}{=} 3 \times 8 - 3 \times 2$	$3(8 \div 2) \stackrel{?}{=} 3 \times 8 \div 3 \times 2$
$3(6) \stackrel{?}{=} 24 - 6$	$3(4) \stackrel{?}{=} 24 \div 6$
$18 = 18$ ✓	$12 \div 4$

3. Does the Distributive Property apply to multiplication over subtraction? Does it apply to multiplication over division? Explain. **The Distributive Property applies to multiplication over subtraction, but does not apply to multiplication over division.**

Chapter 1   58   Course 2

Chapter 1   **A26**   Course 2

Lesson 1-9

NAME _____ DATE _____ PERIOD _____

1-9 Study Guide and Intervention

Algebra: Arithmetic Sequences

An **arithmetic sequence** is a list in which each term is found by adding the same number to the previous term. 1, 3, 5, 7, 9, ...
+2 +2 +2 +2

Example 1 **Describe the relationship between terms in the arithmetic sequence 17, 23, 29, 35, ... Then write the next three terms in the sequence.**

17, 23, 29, 35, ...   Each term is found by adding 6 to the previous term.
+6 +6 +6

$35 + 6 = 41$ $41 + 6 = 47$ $47 + 6 = 53$

The next three terms are 41, 47, and 53.

Example 2

MONEY Brian's parents have decided to start giving him a monthly allowance for one year. Each month they will increase his allowance by $10. Suppose this pattern continues. What algebraic expression can be used to find Brian's allowance after any given number of months? How much money will Brian receive for the 10th month?

Make a table to display the sequence.

Position	Operation	Value of Term
1	$1 \cdot 10$	10
2	$2 \cdot 10$	20
3	$3 \cdot 10$	30
n	$n \cdot 10$	$10n$

Each term is 20 times its position number. So, the expression is $10n$.
How much money will Brian earn after 10 months?
$10n$ Write the expression.
$10(10) = 100$ Replace n with 10

So, for the 10th month Brian will receive $100.

Exercises

Describe the relationship between terms in the arithmetic sequences. Write the next three terms in the sequence.

1. 2, 4, 6, 8, ...   2. 4, 7, 10, 13, ...   3. 0.3, 0.6, 0.9, 1.2, ...
+2; 10, 12, 14   **+3; 16, 19, 22**   **+0.3; 1.5, 1.8, 2.1**

4. 200, 212, 224, 236, ... 5. 1.5, 2.0, 2.5, 3.0, ... 6. 12, 19, 26, 33, ...
+12; 248, 260, 272   **+0.5; 3.5, 4.0, 4.5**   **+7; 40, 47, 54**

7. **SALES** Mama's bakery just opened and is currently selling only two types of pastry. Each month, Mama's bakery will add two more types of pastry to their menu. Suppose this pattern continues. What algebraic expression can be used to find the number of pastries offered after any given number of months? How many pastries will be offered in one year?   **2n; 24**

Chapter 1   61   Course 2

NAME _____ DATE _____ PERIOD _____

1-9 Lesson Reading Guide

Algebra: Arithmetic Sequences

Get Ready for the Lesson

Complete the Mini Lab at the top of page 57 in your textbook. Write your answers below.

1. How many centimeter cubes are used to make each figure? **4, 8, 12**

2. What pattern do you see? Describe it in words.

Each time 4 more cubes are added.

3. Suppose this pattern continues. Complete the table to find the number of cubes needed to make each figure.

Figure	1	2	3	4	5	6	7	8
Cubes Needed	4	8	12	16	20	24	28	32

4. How many cubes would you need to make the 10th figure? Explain your reasoning. **40; For the 9th figure, you need 32 + 4 or 36 cubes and for the 10th figure, you need 36 + 4 or 40 cubes.**

Read the Lesson

Complete each sentence.

5. In an arithmetic sequence, each term is found by _____ the same number to the previous term. **adding**

6. In a geometric sequence, each term is found by _____ the previous term by the same number. **multiplying**

What is the next term in each of the following sequences?

7. 1, 5, 25, ... **125**
   ×5 × 5

8. 7, 10, 13, ... **16**
   + 3 + 3

Remember What You Learned

9. Write down the first four terms of two of your own sequences, an arithmetic sequence and a geometric sequence. Trade with a partner. Describe your partner's sequences. How did you identify the patterns? **See students' work.**

Chapter 1   60   Course 2

Answers

Answers (Lesson 1-9)

Practice panel

1-9 Practice
Algebra: Arithmetic Sequences

Describe the relationship between the terms in each arithmetic sequence. Then write the next three terms in each sequence.

1. 0, 5, 10, 15, …
5 is added to each term;
20, 25, 30

2. 1, 3, 5, 7, …
2 is added to each term;
9, 11, 13

3. 18, 27, 36, 45, …
9 is added to each term;
54, 63, 72

4. 7, 19, 31, 43, …
12 is added to each term;
55, 67, 79

5. 8, 18, 28, 38, …
10 is added to each term;
48, 58, 68

6. 25, 26, 27, 28, …
1 is added to each term;
29, 30, 31

7. 0.4, 0.8, 1.2, 1.6, …
0.4 is added to each term;
2.0, 2.4, 2.8

8. 3.7, 3.7, 3.7, 3.7, …
0 is added to each term;
3.7, 3.7, 3.7

9. 5.1, 6.2, 7.3, 8.4, …
1.1 is added to each term;
9.5, 10.6, 11.7

10. 17, 31, 45, 59, …
14 is added to each term;
73, 87, 101

11. 30, 50, 70, 90, …
20 is added to each term;
110, 130, 150

12. 14, 41, 68, 95, …
27 is added to each term;
122, 149, 176

In a *geometric sequence*, each term is found by multiplying the previous term by the same number. Write the next three terms of each geometric sequence.

13. 5, 10, 20, 40, …
80, 160, 320

14. 3, 9, 27, 81, …
243, 729, 2,187

15. 2, 8, 32, 128, …
512, 2,048, 8,192

NUMBER SENSE Find the 40th term in each arithmetic sequence.

16. 4, 8, 12, 16, …
160

17. 13, 26, 39, 52, …
520

18. 6, 12, 18, 24, …
240

19. **GEOMETRY** The lengths of the sides of a 6-sided polygon are in arithmetic sequence. The length of the shortest side is 3 meters. If the length of the next longer side is 5 meters, what is the length of the longest side?

13 meters

20. **FREE FALLING OBJECT** A free falling object increases speed by a little over 22 miles per hour each second. The arithmetic sequence 22, 44, 66, …, represents the speed after each second, in miles per hour, of a dropped object. How fast is a rock falling after 8 seconds if it is dropped over the side of a cliff?

176 mph

Chapter 1   63   Course 2

Skills Practice panel

1-9 Skills Practice
Algebra: Arithmetic Sequences

Describe the relationship between the terms in each arithmetic sequence.

1. 3, 6, 9, 12, … **+3**

2. 1, 3, 5, 7, … **+2**

3. 1, 2, 3, 4, … **+1**

4. 0, 7, 14, 21, … **+7**

5. 2, 5, 8, 11, … **+3**

6. 5, 10, 15, 20, … **+5**

7. 0.3, 0.6, 0.9, 1.2, … **+0.3**

8. 1, 10, 19, 28, … **+9**

9. 6, 18, 24, 30, … **+6**

10. 0.5, 2.5, 4.5, 6.5, … **+2**

11. 3, 7, 11, 15, … **+4**

12. 0, 4.5, 9, 13.5, … **+4.5**

13. 11, 22, 33, 44, … **+11**

14. 11, 22, 33, 44, … **+11**

Give the next three terms in each sequence.

15. 3, 6, 9, 12, … **15, 18, 21**

16. 18, 21, 24, 27, … **30, 33, 36**

17. 7, 10, 13, 16, … **19, 22, 25**

18. 4, 8, 12, 16, … **20, 24, 28**

19. 0, 7, 14, 21, … **28, 35, 42**

20. 7, 12, 17, 22, … **27, 32, 37**

21. 5, 7, 9, 11, … **13, 15, 17**

22. 5, 15, 25, 35, … **45, 55, 65**

23. 21, 42, 63, 84, … **105, 126, 147**

24. 1.1, 2.2, 3.3, 4.4, … **5.5, 6.6, 7.7**

25. 0.5, 1.0, 1.5, 2.0, … **2.5, 3.0, 3.5**

26. 1.7, 1.9, 2.1, 2.3, … **2.5, 2.7, 2.9**

27. 0.5, 1.5, 2.5, 3.5, … **4.5, 5.5, 6.5**

28. 0.1, 0.2, 0.3, 0.4, … **0.5, 0.6, 0.7**

Chapter 1   62   Course 2

NAME _____ DATE _____ PERIOD _____

1-9 Word Problem Practice
Algebra: Arithmetic Sequences

1. NUMBERS The multiples of two form a sequence as follows: 2, 4, 6, 8, 10, 12, 14, 16, ... Describe the sequence you see? What about the multiples of three? Four? Five? **Arithmetic; the multiples of any number would result in an arithmetic sequence.**

2. OLYMPICS The summer Olympics occur every four years. If the last summer Olympics happened in 2004, when are the next three years that it will occur? Describe the sequence the Olympic years form? **2008, 2012, 2016; arithmetic**

3. BABY-SITTING Tonya charges $3.50 per hour to baby-sit. The sequence $3.50, $7.00, $10.50, $14.00, ... represents how much she charges for each subsequent hour. For example, $10.50 is the third term that represents how much she charges for 3 hours. What are the next three terms in the sequence? How much does she charge for 7 hours of baby-sitting? **$17.50, $21.00, $24.50; $24.50**

4. RECTANGLES Suppose you start with 1 rectangle and then divide it in half. You now have 2 rectangles. You divide each of these in half, and you have 4 rectangles. The sequence for this division is 1, 2, 4, 8, 16, ... rectangles after each successive division. Describe the sequence that results? **geometric**

5. BACTERIA Three bacteria are in a dish. Each hour the number of bacteria multiplies by four. If at the end of the first hour there are 12 bacteria, how many bacteria are there at the end of the next three hours? Describe the sequence that results? **48, 192, 768; geometric**

6. ENROLLMENT The enrollment at Grove Middle School is expected to increase by 40 students each year for the next 5 years. If their current enrollment is 600 students, find their enrollment after each of the next 5 years. **640, 680, 720, 760, 800**

7. SALARY Mrs. Malone's current salary is $1,500. She expects it to increase $100 per year. Write the first 6 terms of a sequence that represents her salary. The first term should be her current salary. What does the sixth term represent? **$1,500, $1,600, $1,700, $1,800, $1,900, $2,000; her salary after 5 years or at the beginning of the sixth year**

8. FIBONACCI The Fibonacci sequence is named after Leonardo Fibonacci who first explored it. Look at the Fibonacci sequence below and describe its pattern. 1, 1, 2, 3, 5, 8, 13, 21, 34, ... **Each term is found by adding the two previous terms; it is neither arithmetic nor geometric.**

NAME _____ DATE _____ PERIOD _____

1-9 Enrichment

Other Sequences

When each term in a sequence decreases, it is described as a *declining sequence*. Either subtracting the same number from the previous term or dividing the previous term by the same number creates a declining sequence.

81, 27, 9, 3, ...
$\div 3 \;\; \div 3 \;\; \div 3$

> In this sequence, each term is found by dividing the previous term by 3.

2, 5, 11, 23, 47, ...
$\times 2 + 1 \;\; \times 2 + 1 \;\; \times 2 + 1 \;\; \times 2 + 1$

> In this sequence, each term is found by multiplying the previous term by 2 and then adding 1.

Some sequences are formed by using two operations.

Describe the rule in each sequence. Then write the next three terms.

1. 40, 38, 36, 34, ... **Subtract 2; 32, 30, 28**

2. 128, 64, 32, 16, ... **Divide by 2; 8, 4, 2**

3. 7.5, 6.4, 5.3, 4.2, ... **Subtract 1.1; 3.1, 2.0, 0.9**

4. 1, 4, 13, 40, ... **Multiply by 3 and add 1; 121, 364, 1093**

5. 1, 5, 13, 61, ... **Multiply by 2 and add 3; 125, 253, 509**

6. 1, 5, 21, 85, ... **Multiply by 4 and add 1; 341, 1365, 5461**

Create a five-term sequence using the rule stated. Start with the given number.

7. Subtract 8 from each term; 78. **78, 70, 62, 54, 46**

8. Divide each term by 10; 80. **80, 8, 0.8, 0.08, 0.008**

9. Subtract 11 from each term; 132. **132, 121, 110, 99, 88**

10. Multiply each term by 10 and subtract 9; 4. **4, 31, 301, 3001, 30,001**

11. Multiply each term by 7 and add 2; 1. **1, 9, 65, 457, 3201**

12. Multiply each term by 3 and subtract 2; 6. **6, 16, 46, 136, 406**

CHALLENGE For Exercises 13–15, use the sequence 589, 5,889, 58,889, 588,889, ...

13. Describe the rule of the sequence. **Multiply each term by 10 and subtract 1.**

14. Study the pattern in the sequence. Without extending the sequence, what is the sixth term of the sequence? **58,888,889** What is the tenth term? **588,888,888,889**

15. Describe how you can find any term of the sequence. **Sample answer: The nth term starts with 5, followed by n eights, and ends with 9.**

Lesson 1-9

Answers

1-9 Scientific Calculator Activity

NAME _____ DATE _____ PERIOD _____

Geometric Sequences

A geometric sequence is a list in which each term is found by *multiplying* the previous term by the same number.

$$2, \underset{\times 3}{\overset{\frown}{}} 6, \underset{\times 3}{\overset{\frown}{}} 18, \underset{\times 3}{\overset{\frown}{}} 54, \ldots$$

n = 3   n = 6   n = 12   n = 24

Look for a pattern in the groups of dots above. Can you see that each time the number of dots doubles? The number of dots in each group forms the *geometric sequence* 3, 6, 12, 24. In a geometric sequence, the numbers are related by multiplication.

Example **Find the next three numbers in the geometric sequence: 0.8, 2.4, 7.2, 21.6.**

Divide the second term by the first term to find the *common ratio*.

Enter: 2.4 ÷ 0.8 ENTER = 3

Multiply the last term by the common ratio to find the next term.

Enter: 21.6 × 3 ENTER = 64.8

Repeat the last step until you get all of the terms.

Enter: 64.8 × 3 ENTER = 194.4

Enter: 194.4 × 3 ENTER = 583.2

The next three terms are 64.8, 194.4, and 583.2.

Exercises

Find the next three terms in each geometric sequence.

1. 0.1, 0.01, 0.001
   0.0001, 0.00001,
   0.000001

2. 8, 1.6, 0.32
   0.064, 0.0128,
   0.00256

3. 12, 54, 243
   1,093.5, 4,920.75,
   22,143.375

4. 18, 27, 40.5
   60.75, 91.125,
   136.6875

5. 2.1, 0.42, 0.084
   0.0168, 0.00336,
   0.000672

6. 256, 128, 64
   32, 16, 8

7. 0.05, 0.1, 0.2
   0.4, 0.8, 1.6

8. 8.4, 0.84, 0.084
   0.0084, 0.00084,
   0.000084

9. 9, 31.5, 110.25
   385.875,
   1,350.5625,
   4,726.96875

Chapter 1   66   *Course 2*

1-10 Lesson Reading Guide

NAME _____ DATE _____ PERIOD _____

Algebra: Equations and Functions

Get Ready for the Lesson

Read the introduction at the top of page 63 in your textbook. Write your answers below.

1. Complete the table to find the cost of 2, 3, and 4 magazines.

Magazines		
Number	Multiply by 4	Cost($)
1	4 × 1	4
2	4 × 2	8
3	4 × 3	12
4	4 × 4	16

2. Describe the pattern in the table between the cost and the number of magazines.
   The cost increases by 4 each time the number of magazines increases by 1.

Read the Lesson

3. Complete each function table. Then identify the domain and range.

a.

x	2x − 1	y
−1	2(−1) − 1	−3
0	2(0) − 1	−1
1	2(1) − 1	1

domain: {−1, 0, 1}
range: {−3, −1, 1}

b.

x	4x	y
−1	4(−1)	−4
0	4(0)	0
1	4(1)	4

domain: {−1, 0, 1}
range: {−4, 0, 4}

4. **MONEY** John earns $15 per lawn that he mows.
   a. Write an equation in two variables showing the relationship between lawns mowed and the money John earns.
      m = lawns mowed, d = dollars earned, 15m = d
   b. How much money does John earn after mowing 3, 5, and 10 lawns?
      3, $45 5, $75 10, $150

Remember What You Learned

5. Draw a picture of a "machine" that shows how a function works. Your picture should illustrate input, a function rule, and output. **See students' work.**

Chapter 1   67   *Course 2*

NAME _____ DATE _____ PERIOD _____

1-10 Skills Practice

Algebra: Equations and Functions

Copy and complete each function table. Identify the domain and range.

1. $y = x - 1$

x	x − 1	y
1	1 − 1	0
2	2 − 1	1
3	3 − 1	2
4	4 − 1	3

domain: {1, 2, 3, 4}
range: {0, 1, 2, 3}

2. $y = x + 7$

x	x + 7	y
1	1 + 7	8
2	2 + 7	9
3	3 + 7	10
4	4 + 7	11

domain: {1, 2, 3, 4}
range: {8, 9, 10, 11}

3. $y = 3x$

x	3x	y
1	3(1)	3
2	3(2)	6
3	3(3)	9
4	3(4)	12

domain: {1, 2, 3, 4}
range: {3, 6, 9, 12}

4. $y = 4x$

x	4x	y
2	4(2)	8
3	4(3)	12
4	4(4)	16
5	4(5)	20

domain: {2, 3, 4, 5}
range: {8, 12, 16, 20}

5. $y = x - 0.5$

x	x − 0.5	y
1	1 − 0.5	0.5
2	2 − 0.5	1.5
3	3 − 0.5	2.5
4	4 − 0.5	3.5

domain: {1, 2, 3, 4}
range: {0.5, 1.5, 2.5, 3.5}

6. $y = 10x$

x	10x	y
0	10(0)	0
1	10(1)	10
2	10(2)	20
3	10(3)	30

domain: {0, 1, 2, 3}
range: {0, 10, 20, 30}

Solve each word problem.

For Exercises 7 and 8, use the following information.

TRAVEL For every gallon of gas, a car can travel 30 miles.

7. Write an equation using two variables to show the relationship between the distance the car travels and the gallons of gas it uses.
$d = $ distance, $g = $ gallons of gas, $30g = d$

8. If a car had 8 gallons of gas left in its tank, how many miles can it travel before the tank runs out?
240 miles

For Exercises 9 and 10, use the following information.

FARMING Every row of corn in Mr. Jones' garden has 5 cornstalks.

9. Write an equation using two variables to show the relationship between the number of rows and the number of cornstalks.
$r = $ rows, $s = $ stalks, $5r = s$

10. If Mr. Jones has 7 rows of corn, how many cornstalks will he need to harvest?
35 cornstalks

Chapter 1   69   *Course 2*

NAME _____ DATE _____ PERIOD _____

1-10 Study Guide and Intervention

Algebra: Equations and Functions

The solution of an equation with two variables consists of two numbers, one for each variable that makes the equation true. When a relationship assigns exactly one output value for each input value, it is called a function. Function tables help to organize input numbers, output numbers, and function rules.

Example 1 Complete a function table for $y = 5x$. Then state the domain and range.

Choose four values for x. Substitute the values for x into the expression. Then evaluate to find the y value.

x	5x	y
0	5(0)	0
1	5(1)	5
2	5(2)	10
3	5(3)	15

The domain is {0, 1, 2, 3}. The range is {0, 5, 10, 15}.

Exercises

Complete the following function tables. Then state the domain and range.

1. $y = x + 4$

x	x + 4	y
0	0+4	4
1	1+4	5
2	2+4	6
3	3+4	7

domain: {0, 1, 2, 3}
range: {4, 5, 6, 7}

2. $y = 10x$

x	10x	y
1	10(1)	10
2	10(2)	20
3	10(3)	30
4	10(4)	40

domain: {1, 2, 3, 4}
range: {10, 20, 30, 40}

3. $y = x - 1$

x	x − 1	y
2	2−1	1
3	3−1	2
4	4−1	3
5	5−1	4

domain: {2, 3, 4, 5}
range: {1, 2, 3, 4}

4. $y = 3x$

x	3x	y
10	3(10)	30
11	3(11)	33
12	3(12)	36
13	3(13)	39

domain: {10, 11, 12, 13}
range: {30, 33, 36, 39}

Chapter 1   68   *Course 2*

Answers (Lesson 1-10)

1-10 Word Problem Practice
Algebra: Equations and Functions

1. **TECHNOLOGY** The fee for your pager service is $22 per month. Make a function table that shows your total charge for 1, 2, 3, and 4 months of service.

x, Months	y, Total Charge
1	22
2	44
3	66
4	88

2. **MEASUREMENT** Joe takes 2 steps for every one step that Kim takes. Write an equation in two variables showing the relationship between Joe's steps and Kim's steps. If Kim takes 15 steps, how many steps will Joe have to take to cover the same distance?

$j =$ the number of steps Joe takes

$k =$ the number of steps Kim takes, $2k = j$

30 steps

3. **TRAINS** Between Hiroshima and Kokura, Japan, the bullet train averages a speed of 164 miles per hour, which is the fastest scheduled train service in the world. Make a function table that shows the distance traveled at that speed in 1, 2, 3, and 4 hours.

x, Hours	y, Distance
1	164
2	328
3	492
4	656

4. **BUSINESS** Grant earns $5 for each magazine that he sells. Write an equation in two variables showing the relationship between the number of magazines sold and the amount of money made. If Grant sells 12 magazines, how much money will he make?

$m =$ the number of magazines sold, $d =$ Grant's earnings in dollars, $5m = d$

$60

5. **GEOMETRY** The formula for the volume of a rectangular prism whose base has an area of 8 square units is $V = 8h$, where V is the volume and h is the height. Make a function table that shows the volume of a rectangular prism with a height of 3, 4, 5, and 6 units.

h	8h	V
3	8(3)	24
4	8(4)	32
5	8(5)	40
6	8(6)	48

6. **GEOMETRY** The fastest insect in the world is the dragonfly with a top speed of 36 miles per hour. Write an equation in two variables describing the relationship between the length of the dragonfly's flight and the distance traveled. If a dragonfly flies for 3 hours, how far can he travel?

$y =$ time, $d =$ distance, $36t = d$

108 miles

1-10 Practice
Algebra: Equations and Functions

Complete each function table. Then identify the domain and range.

1. $y = 5x$

x	5x	y
1	5·1	5
2	5·2	10
3	5·3	15
4	5·4	20

Domain: {1, 2, 3, 4}
Range: {5, 10, 15, 20}

2. $y = 8x$

x	8x	y
1	8·1	1
2	8·2	16
3	8·3	24
4	8·4	32

Domain: {1, 2, 3, 4}
Range: {1, 16, 24, 32}

3. $y = 7x$

x	7x	y
3	7·3	21
4	7·4	28
5	7·5	35
6	7·6	42

Domain: {3, 4, 5, 6}
Range: {21, 28, 35, 42}

4. $y = x - 2$

x	x − 2	y
2	2 − 2	0
3	3 − 2	1
4	4 − 2	2
5	5 − 2	3

Domain: {2, 3, 4, 5}
Range: {0, 1, 2, 3}

5. $y = x + 3$

x	x + 3	y
2	2 + 3	5
3	3 + 3	6
4	4 + 3	7
5	5 + 3	8

Domain: {2, 3, 4, 5}
Range: {5, 6, 7, 8}

6. $y = x + 0.75$

x	x + 0.75	y
0	0 + 0.75	0.75
1	1 + 0.75	1.75
2	2 + 0.75	2.75
3	3 + 0.75	3.75

Domain: {0, 1, 2, 3}
Range: {0.75, 1.75, 2.75, 3.75}

7. **PRODUCTION** A car manufacturer makes 15,000 hybrid cars a month. Using the function table, find the number of hybrid cars produced after 3, 6, 9, and 12 months.

m	15,000m	P
3	15,000 · 3	45,000
6	15,000 · 6	90,000
9	15,000 · 9	135,000
12	15,000 · 12	180,000

8. **SUNSPOTS** The changing activity of sunspots, which are cooler and darker areas of the sun, occur in 11-year cycles. Use the function $y = 11c$ to find the numbers of years necessary to complete 1, 2, 3, and 4 sunspot cycles.

11 years, 22 years, 33 years, and 44 years

NAME _____ DATE _____ PERIOD _____

1-10 Enrichment

To solve equations containing two variables, find ordered pair solutions for the equation by selecting values for x and completing a table. Although any value can be selected for x, values usually selected include -2, -1, 0, 1, and 2.

For example, to solve the equation $y = 2x$ given below in Exercise 1, first select values for x, then complete a table.

Ordered pair solutions for the equation $y = 2x$ include $(-2, -4)$, $(-1, -2)$, $(0, 0)$, $(1, 2)$, and $(2, 4)$.

Match each equation with the point whose coordinates are a solution of the equation. Then, at the bottom of the page, write the letter of the point on the line directly above the number of the equation each time it appears. (The first one has been done as an example.) If you have matched the equations and solutions correctly, the letters below will reveal a message.

1. $y = 2x$ $A(-3, 8)$ $N(-1, 0)$
2. $y = x - 3$ $B(0, 2)$ $O(3, 0)$
3. $y = -x + 1$ $C(-2, 1)$ $P(1, 5)$
4. $y = 3x - 2$ $D(0, -5)$ $Q(0, 6)$
5. $y = -2x - 4$ $E(-1, -5)$ $R(1, 6)$
6. $y = x + (-2)$ $F(1, 3)$ $S(2, 1)$
7. $y = -4x - 1$ $G(0, -4)$ $T(-2, 3)$
8. $y = \frac{1}{2}x$ $H(-1, 3)$ $U(1, 2)$
9. $y = x + 3$ $I(2, 0)$ $V(-3, 5)$
10. $y = 7x + 7$ $J(0, 4)$ $W(0, -7)$
11. $y = -2x - 6$ $K(-3, 1)$ $X(-3, -3)$
12. $y = -x + 5$ $L(-4, 2)$ $Y(1, 8)$
13. $y = -5x + 8$ $M(-2, 2)$ $Z(0, -8)$
14. $y = -x$

M	A	T	H	E	M	A	T	I	C	S		I	S		T	H	E
14	12	3	7	4	14	12	3	6	9	8		6	8		3	7	4

L	A	N	G	U	A	G	E		O	F		S	C	I	E	N	C	E
11	12	10	5	1	12	5	4		2	13		4	9	6	4	10	9	4

NAME _____ DATE _____ PERIOD _____

1-10 TI-73 Activity
Function Tables

Create function tables with a TI-73 graphing calculator by using the LIST feature.

Example Create a function table for the function rule $3n + 2$. Use input values -4, 2, 0, and 5.

Step 1 Clear all lists.
2nd [MEM] 6 ENTER

Step 2 Create a new list in a blank-list position. LIST

Step 3 Label the list INPUT.
2nd [TEXT] I N P U T Done ENTER ENTER

Step 4 Enter the input values: -4, 2, 0, and 5. Press ENTER after each value.

Step 5 Create another list in a different blank-list position. Label it OUTPUT. (See step 3.)

Step 6 Enter the function rule, $3n + 2$, in the OUTPUT list.
2nd [STAT] (choose the list INPUT)
3 X 2nd [TEXT] " Done
+ 2 2nd [TEXT] " Done ENTER ENTER

Step 7 Observe the values in the OUTPUT list. Choose 3 more input values. Observe the corresponding output values.

```
L6   INPUT  OUTPU◆B
     -4     B-10
      2      8
      0      2
      5      17

OUTPUT(1)=-10
```

Exercises
Enter them in the INPUT list. Observe the output values.

Complete each function table.

1.

Input (n)	Output (-4n)
-3	12
-1	4
0	0
1	-4
3	-12

2.

Input (n)	Output $\left(\frac{-n}{2}\right)$
-24	12
-10	5
15	-7.5
30	-15
45	-22.5

3.

Input (n)	Output (-2n - 6)
12	-30
8	-22
3	-12
-7	8
-15	24

4.

Input (n)	Output (-3n + 1)	Output (6n - 8)
15	-44	82
10	-29	52
6	-17	28
-25	76	-158
-32	97	-200

Chapter 1 Assessment Answer Key

Quiz 1 (Lessons 1-1 through 1-3)
Page 77

1. subtraction and division
2. $17
3. 81
4. 64
5. 100,000
6. 5 · 5 · 5
7. 529
8. 1,849
9. 1,296
10. 19

Quiz 2 (Lessons 1-4 and 1-5)
Page 77

1. 55
2. 15
3. 52
4. 3(0.79) + 1.05
5. 4

Quiz 3 (Lessons 1-6 through 1-8)
Page 78

1. 10
2. 4
3. 9
4. 16
5. Associative Property of Addition

Quiz 4 (Lessons 1-9 and 1-10)
Page 78

1. 5 is added to each term; 21, 26, 31
2. 4 is added to each term; 45, 49, 53
3. C
4. $f = s - 7$
5. 25

Mid-Chapter Test
Page 79

1. C
2. F
3. B
4. J
5. A
6. 256
7. coefficient: 3; variable: s; constant: −7
8. 500 seats
9. 3^5
10. 10^4
11. 256
12. 343
13. 170 students

Chapter 1 Assessment Answer Key

Vocabulary Test
Page 80

1. arithmetic sequence
2. square
3. radical sign
4. algebraic expression
5. coefficient
6. exponent
7. order of operations
8. equation
9. function
10. range
11. a number that makes an equation true
12. a letter that stands for an unknown value

Form 1
Page 81

1. B
2. F
3. B
4. H
5. A
6. J
7. D
8. G
9. A
10. G
11. C
12. G
13. B

Page 82

14. J
15. B
16. H
17. D
18. G
19. B
20. J
21. C
22. H
23. A
24. H
25. D
B: 2

Chapter 1 Assessment Answer Key

Form 2A
Page 83

1. __B__
2. __H__
3. __A__
4. __G__
5. __D__
6. __G__
7. __C__
8. __H__
9. __B__
10. __H__
11. __C__
12. __G__
13. __D__

Page 84

14. __F__
15. __C__
16. __G__
17. __B__
18. __J__
19. __B__
20. __F__
21. __C__
22. __J__
23. __C__
24. __H__
25. __D__

B: 3(0.79) +
4(1.39); $7.93

Form 2B
Page 85

1. __A__
2. __G__
3. __D__
4. __F__
5. __D__
6. __H__
7. __C__
8. __H__
9. __C__
10. __G__
11. __A__
12. __H__
13. __A__

Page 86

14. __J__
15. __B__
16. __G__
17. __B__
18. __H__
19. __B__
20. __F__
21. __D__
22. __G__
23. __C__
24. __F__
25. __A__

B: 4(0.75) +
3(1.59); $7.77

Chapter 1 Assessment Answer Key

Form 2C
Page 87

1. 10,500 people

2. $4 \cdot 4 \cdot 4 \cdot 4 \cdot 4$

3. 128

4. 3^5

5. 81

6. 1,600

7. 12

8. 37

9. 14

10. 64

11. 17

12. 68

13. 3 Q, 3 D, 2 N

14. 24

15. 5

16. 17

17. 15

18. 15

19. 50

Page 88

20. 42

21. 27

22. $r = 14 + 3$;
17 laps

23. $1.55 + m = 2.75$;
$1.20

24. $(9)7 + (2)7$; 77

25. $3(12) - 3(5)$; 21

26. Associative Property of Multiplication

27. Identity Property of Addition

28. 2.5 is added to each term.

29. 7 is added to each term.

30. 15.4, 18.4, 21.4

31. 30, 36, 42

32. $y = 7x$

33. $105

Chapter 1 Assessment Answer Key

Form 2D
Page 89

Page 90

1. 3,600 annuals

2. 3 · 3 · 3 · 3 · 3 · 3

3. 125

4. 7^5

5. 16

6. 900

7. 11

8. 33

9. 15

10. 12

11. 19

12. 30

13. 4Q, 3D, 1N

14. 49

15. 4

16. 8

17. 12

18. 18

19. 80

20. 39

21. 48

22. $r = 6 + 4$; 10 laps

23. $1.15 + h = 2.85$, $1.70

24. $(7)5 + (3)5$; 50

25. $4(10) - 4(7)$; 12

26. Commutative Property of Addition

27. Identity Property of Multiplication

28. 2.1 is added to each term.

29. 5 is added to each term.

30. 25.3, 30.3, 35.3

31. 36, 44, 52

32. $y = 8x$

33. $176

B: ×; −; ÷

Chapter 1 Assessment Answer Key

Form 3
Page 91

1. ___19 departures___

2. ___5 plants___

3. ___169___

4. ___3^6___

5. ___$7^3 \cdot 2^4$___

6. ___361___

7. ___1,024___

8. ___21___

9. ___16___

10. ___12___

11. ___75___

12. ___$40 \div (2 + 8) - 2 = 2$___

13. ___65 bracelets and 35 buttons___

14. Sample answer: An equation has an equals sign, and an expression does not. expression: $x + 8$; equation: $x + 8 = 15$

15. ___40___

Page 92

16. ___$1; \frac{8}{3}; 4; f = 3y$ or $y = \frac{1}{3}f$___

17. ___20___

18. ___162___

19. ___They are equal.___

20. ___$17 + 8b$___

21. ___$9z + 63$___

22. ___5 is added to each term; 37, 42, 47___

23. ___9 is added to each term; 40.5, 49.5, 58.5___

24. ___1.3 is added to each term; 10.2, 11.5, 12.8___

25. ___$m = 35h$; 122.5 mi___

B: ___$14 + 2a$___

Chapter 1 Assessment Answer Key

Page 93, Extended-Response Test
Scoring Rubric

Level	Specific Criteria
4	The student demonstrates a **thorough understanding** of the mathematics concepts and/or procedures embodied in the task. The student has responded correctly to the task, used mathematically sound procedures, and provided clear and complete explanations and interpretations. The response may contain minor flaws that do not detract from the demonstration of a thorough understanding.
3	The student demonstrates an **understanding** of the mathematics concepts and/or procedures embodied in the task. The student's response to the task is essentially correct with the mathematical procedures used and the explanations and interpretations provided demonstrating an essential but less than thorough understanding. The response may contain minor errors that reflect inattentive execution of the mathematical procedures or indications of some misunderstanding of the underlying mathematics concepts and/or procedures.
2	The student has demonstrated only a **partial understanding** of the mathematics concepts and/or procedures embodied in the task. Although the student may have used the correct approach to obtaining a solution or may have provided a correct solution, the student's work lacks an essential understanding of the underlying mathematical concepts. The response contains errors related to misunderstanding important aspects of the task, misuse of mathematical procedures, or faulty interpretations of results.
1	The student has demonstrated a **very limited understanding** of the mathematics concepts and/or procedures embodied in the task. The student's response to the task is incomplete and exhibits many flaws. Although the student has addressed some of the conditions of the task, the student reached an inadequate conclusion and/or provided reasoning that was faulty or incomplete. The response exhibits many errors or may be incomplete.
0	The student has provided a **completely incorrect** solution or uninterpretable response, or no response at all.

Chapter 1 Assessment Answer Key

Page 93, Extended-Response Test
Sample Answers

In addition to the scoring rubric found on page A31, the following sample answers may be used as guidance in evaluating open-ended assessment items.

1. $7p + 6(p \div q)^2 - 2q = 7(6) + 6(6 \div 3)^2 - 2(3)$ Replace p with 6 and q with 3.

$= 7(6) + 6(2)^2 - 2(3)$ Divide first since $6 \div 3$ is in parentheses.

$= 7(6) + 6(4) - 2(3)$ Find the value of 2^2.

$= 42 + 24 - 6$ Multiply.

$= 66 - 6$ Add from left to right, $42 + 24$.

$= 60$ Subtract $66 - 6$.

2. a. Let t represent the total number of tickets purchased. $t = 25 + 5$; 30 tickets

   b. Sample answer:

Understand	Find the total cost of tickets for 25 students and 5 adults if student tickets cost \$4 each and adult tickets cost \$6 each.
Plan	Multiply the number of tickets of each type by the cost for each type of ticket and add the results.
Solve	25 student tickets $\times$ \$4 = \$100 5 adult tickets $\times$ \$6 = \$30 \$100 + \$30 = \$130 The teacher spent \$130 on tickets.
Check	For 30 people, \$130 is a reasonable amount to spend on tickets given the prices of \$4 and \$6 per ticket.

3. 752, 756, 760, 764, 768

        $+4$ $+4$ $+4$ $+4$

Each term is found by adding 4 to the previous term. The next term can be found by adding 4 to the last term.
$768 + 4 = 772$

4. The square root of a number is one of its two equal factors.

Chapter 1 Assessment Answer Key

Page 95

1. Ⓐ Ⓑ Ⓒ ●

2. Ⓕ Ⓖ ● Ⓙ

3. Ⓐ Ⓑ ● Ⓓ

4. Ⓕ Ⓖ Ⓗ ●

5. Ⓐ Ⓑ ● Ⓓ

6. ● Ⓖ Ⓗ Ⓙ

7. Ⓐ Ⓑ ● Ⓓ

8. Ⓕ Ⓖ ● Ⓙ

9. Ⓐ ● Ⓒ Ⓓ

10. Ⓕ Ⓖ Ⓗ ●

11. ● Ⓑ Ⓒ Ⓓ

12. Ⓕ Ⓖ Ⓗ ●

13. Ⓐ Ⓑ Ⓒ ●

14. ● Ⓖ Ⓗ Ⓙ

15. ● Ⓑ Ⓒ Ⓓ

16. Ⓕ ● Ⓗ Ⓙ

17. Ⓐ Ⓑ ● Ⓓ

18. Ⓕ Ⓖ ● Ⓙ

Chapter 1 Assessment Answer Key

19. _____ 6 mi _____

20. _____ 3 _____

21. _____ 9 _____

22. _____ 30 _____

23. ___ Commutative ___

24. ___ 60 revolutions ___

25a. _____ yes _____

25b. _____ 1:45 P.M. _____

25c. ___ Yes; Sample answer: The roast bakes for 2 hours, then cools for 15 minutes. ___

Answers